WHAT ARE COSMIC RAYS?

WHAT ARE COSMIC RAYS?

Revised and Enlarged American Edition

BY PIERRE AUGER

TRANSLATED FROM THE FRENCH
by
MAURICE M. SHAPIRO

UNIVERSITY OF CHICAGO PRESS · CHICAGO

University of Chicago Press · Chicago 37
Agent: Cambridge University Press · London

Copyright 1945 by The University of Chicago. All rights reserved. Published January 1945. Third Impression December 1945. Composed and printed by the University of Chicago Press Chicago, Illinois, U.S.A.

PREFACE

THIS book is written primarily for the reader who lacks
a technical knowledge of physics but who wants to keep
in touch with current developments in science. It is not in-
tended for the specialist but should provide a good perspec-
tive for the physicist who wants to get a quick view of what
has been done in this new field. It is as simple and straight-
forward as the nature of the subject and the vast amount of
material available will permit.

It is the only volume in English which gives a broad and
up-to-date discussion of all the major cosmic-ray phenomena.
The treatment of its topics is, in general, nonmathematical
and is designed both to provide the background and to describe the outstanding developments in the field. The author
first introduces the reader to the modern techniques which
enable the physicist to detect subatomic particles. The story
of cosmic rays is then traced from the time of their discovery to the most recent stratospheric balloon flights. The author recounts the various problems which have confronted
the investigators of cosmic rays and describes how they went
about solving them. He does not neglect to point out the
main problems which are yet unsolved.

Originally published under the title of *Rayons cosmiques*
by the Presses Universitaires de France, Paris, in 1941, the
work has now been completely revised and brought up to
date in the light of important changes and new discoveries

in the field of cosmic rays. The drawings and plates have also been revised and supplemented from new material generously provided by scientists in the United States. In accordance with the author's wishes, the translation is a very free one, for the sake of conforming to English scientific usage and of improving the clarity for the general reader.

It is a pleasure to thank Dean Arthur H. Compton and Professor Marcel Schein for reading the manuscript and offering valuable criticism. I am also grateful to my wife, Inez Shapiro, for her generous assistance.

MAURICE M. SHAPIRO

CHICAGO, ILLINOIS
October 15, 1944

TABLE OF CONTENTS

CHAPTER ONE

Story of a Discovery

SO REMARKABLY has science extended our powers of perception that we have virtually acquired a set of new senses. As a matter of fact, the sense organs with which nature has provided us are useful in a very limited domain; and indeed many kinds of phenomena escape us altogether, since they produce no perceptible effects. Thus our eye responds to only those vibrations of light whose wave-lengths lie between 0.4 and 0.7 microns (there are 25,400 microns in 1 inch), a narrow region bracketed by bands of radiations—infra-red and ultra-violet—to which we are blind. None of our organs is directly sensitive to ultrasonic waves, to the electromagnetic waves in the radio bands, or to radiations from radioactive substances.

A SIXTH SENSE

These deficiencies are largely overcome by the technician equipped with appropriate detectors which transform these radiations into other kinds of waves perceptible to the eye or ear so that he can detect them indirectly. The observer, however, tends to lose sight of the intermediate apparatus, and soon he talks of "hearing" wireless waves or "seeing" ultra-violet rays.

If, then, we are to conquer the domain of subatomic phe-

1

nomena, we must invoke a chain of intermediate events which can transform the effects of the original radiations into perceptible ones. Even these effects, however, must be amplified, for our senses cannot respond to excitations below a certain threshold of intensity. It is necessary, in most of the transformations with which we are concerned, to multiply the feeble energy produced initially until it exceeds our sensory threshold. By combining such techniques of detection and amplification, it has been possible, in certain cases, to bring phenomena of atomic dimensions within the range of our senses. We have, in effect, been enabled to "see" or "hear" the passage of a single electron, the disintegration of an atomic nucleus, and the absorption of a photon by an atom.

Let us examine several of these intermediary chains of events which have led physicists to an understanding of subatomic phenomena undreamed of several decades ago. The vital link in each chain is the ion—the atom or molecule which carries an electric charge. It is this charge which makes the ion the key to modern atomic physics. Suppose we wish to detect a beam of atoms or electrons. We must depend on one of the effects it produces while traversing the matter in our apparatus, and the only direct effect is generally a production of ions. We shall first examine the circumstances of such production; and then we shall see how the ions can be recognized, counted, measured, and used.

Let us shoot an electronic projectile through a substance. What happens as the tiny "bullet" forces its way through the aggregation of atoms in a gas, through the dense mass of molecules in a liquid, or through the orderly array of atoms in a crystalline solid? To get an idea of the effects produced, we might compare our electronic projectile to a crazy motorcyclist driving full speed through a crowd of people or through a regiment of troops in military formation. His great momentum enables the cyclist to ram his way through these crowds, leaving in his wake a host of shattered arms and fractured legs. Suppose we witnessed this carnage from a high-flying airplane. Though the cyclist himself would not be clearly visible, we could trace the path of his incursion by the row of fallen victims left behind.

In the world of atoms, these victims represent ions, i.e., atoms or molecules bereft of one or more electrons by collision with the fast particle. Even in their normal state, these atoms and molecules are highly agitated. As they lose their electrical neutrality they acquire distinctive properties, which enable us to detect them. The separated electrons may remain free for some time; but generally they are soon captured by neutral molecules, whereby the latter are transformed into negative ions. The presence of these ions, these charged corpuscles, is the only trace left by the speedy electronic bullet.

ON THE TRAIL OF THE ION

Just how are these ions manifest in our apparatus? Placed in an electric field—to which their charge is responsive—they go into action, moving toward the positive or negative electrode, depending upon the sign of their charge. In so doing, they transport a current; this is the process of electrical convection. A gas or liquid which is normally insulating becomes conducting when ions are created within it; the medium is then said to be "ionized." Now, it is well known that electrical measurements are among the most sensitive ones in physics. Thus one could contrive a simple detector of ionizing rays by inclosing a volume of gas or liquid between two electrodes, thereby forming an "ionization chamber" (Fig. 1). One could then connect the electrodes to the terminals of a source of electrical potential and introduce into the circuit a current-measuring instrument. As the potential establishes an electric field between the electrodes, we need only to expose the gas to the rays we wish to study, and to measure—often after suitable amplification—the current obtained. The value of this current, depending directly on the number of ion-carriers, provides a measure of the ionization.

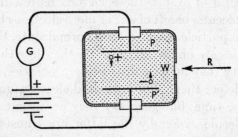

Fig. 1.—Diagram of an ionization chamber. *P, P′*, plates serving as electrodes; *R*, ionizing radiation penetrating the window, *W*, which is much thinner than the walls of the chamber; *G*, an instrument which measures the current.

The ions produced in a gas by ionizing radiations are set in motion by the electric field as soon as they appear. The number of ions created each second in a cubic centimeter is an accurate measure of the ionizing power of the rays. In consequence, it has become customary to measure ionization in "ions per cubic centimeter per second."[1] But one should not forget that the charge on each ion is very minute and that if a gas were bombarded with only a few particles per hour, or

[1] The number of ions produced by a given radiation is proportional to the pressure of the gas, so that the unit actually employed is ions per cubic centimeter per second at atmospheric pressure. It must be added that not all the ions initially produced by the radiation contribute to the measured current. Some of them, encountering ions of opposite charge, may have "recombined," thereby returning to the state of neutral molecules. This effect varies with conditions such as the pressure, the humidity, and the nature of the ionized gas.

even per minute, the resulting ion current would be inappreciable; it would need to be amplified in order to be detected.

This problem has led to the invention of a marvelously simple and sensitive apparatus, the Geiger-Müller "counter." Picture a metallic tube closed at each end by an insulating disk which supports an axial conducting wire (Fig. 2). The

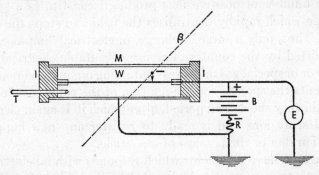

FIG. 2.—Diagram of a Geiger-Müller counter. M, metallic cylinder, and W, axial wire, are the two electrodes; I, insulating plugs; T, tube through which the gas is evacuated to a pressure of a few centimeters of mercury; B, battery which supplies the necessary voltage; R, resistance which quenches the discharge started by an ionizing ray, β; E, electroscope which detects the electrical pulse. This electroscope may be replaced by a vacuum-tube amplifier.

air is pumped out of the tube until a pressure of about $\frac{1}{10}$ atmosphere is reached, and we now have an instrument which can count electrons, one by one.

Let us see how this is possible. Establish a strong electric field between the wire and the tube. Since the gas is an insulator, no current passes. But suppose that an electron, furnished, say, by a radioactive disintegration, gives rise to a single ion in the gas (or rather, a single pair of ions, because a neutral atom, when ionized, breaks up into two parts with opposite charges—one positive and the other negative). At once this ion starts moving. If the field is strong enough, the ion attains sufficient speed to become an ionizing agent along its way. It breaks up the atoms it strikes and transforms them into ions. These, in turn, are set into motion, and soon there is an avalanche of secondary ions giving rise to a noticeable current. However, this current is short-lived, since the large number of positive ions produced constitutes a space charge which rapidly neutralizes the field and stops the current. Thus, only a surge of charge, or electrical "impulse," is permitted by the counter. The use of suitable electrical devices or of special gas mixtures containing organic compounds prevents the spontaneous re-ignition of the counter before a certain very short dead period, after which it is again cleared of all stray ions and is ready to register any new ion-pair creation due to the passage of a particle.

We thus have a detector which responds with an electrical pulse to the passage of single particles, provided that these are charged and sufficiently energetic. This device is generally connected to an amplifier which augments the electrical impulse generated by the ions. As we shall see, special artifices are needed to detect neutral particles, since these do not produce ionization along their path. The "photons," or quanta of electromagnetic radiation, are detected only by the charged particles which they produce in the walls or the gas of the apparatus.

Here, then, are the first two kinds of apparatus based on ionization. The ionization chamber measures the total intensity of an ionizing beam, while the counter tube responds to the passage of the single particles of which the beam is composed. A third method, even more effective, makes the path of the charged particle plainly visible—we refer to the expansion technique of C. T. R. Wilson. This method has played a role of unique importance in the development of modern physics—on the one hand, by providing a powerful instrument of discovery; on the other hand, by furnishing pictorial evidence, as it were, of the movement of electrons, protons, or other ions. Let us return to our simile in which a motorcyclist driving through a dense crowd represented a charged particle traversing matter. Immediately after the passage of the motorcycle, clusters of people gather around to help the wounded. The aggregation of these groups results in a sort of "spatial amplification," which makes it easy for us in the airplane to locate the casualties.

In order to achieve such amplification, Wilson used a gas supersaturated with water vapor. When ions are created in such a gas, they serve as centers of condensation. It is then sufficient to cool rapidly a volume of humid air[2] until it passes the saturation point and then to shoot ionizing particles through it. When the vapor becomes supersaturated, fog appears, each ion becoming the center of a droplet of water, which grows large enough to be visible if well illuminated. The row of droplets delineates the row of ions, thus revealing the path of the particle. Remarkable powers of investigation are opened up by this simple method.

To appreciate the import of this tool, think of the vast information it has yielded concerning the movement of fast electrons—of their collisions, their deflections, their changes in speed, and their other diverse adventures—while passing through matter. Figure 3 shows a diagram of a cloud chamber.

A variant of this method is one in which particles traverse not a vapor but the emulsion of a photographic plate. Each grain of silver bromide encountered by the charged particle

[2] This cooling is usually produced by a sudden increase in volume—an expansion; hence the name "expansion method."

is converted to silver during development. The row of grains so obtained reproduces the peculiarities of the ionizing particle's path. To be sure, these various methods may be combined, as we shall see later, to give a more complete analysis

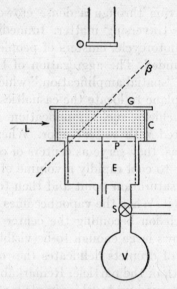

FIG. 3.—Diagram of a Wilson cloud chamber. *P*, piston which suddenly drops to the position shown by the dotted line when the stopcock, *S*, is opened, connecting the space *E* with the evacuated vessel, *V; G*, glass cover cemented to the glass cylinder, *C; L*, light illuminating the fog droplets which condense upon the ions created by a fast electron, *β; O*, objective lens of the photographic apparatus.

and description of the ionization phenomena occurring in matter.

It is no exaggeration to say that we have acquired a sixth sense—the sense of ionization. It apprises us of the appearance of ions and enables us to locate and count them. We thus learn of the passage of charged particles by the trains of ions they leave in their wake. Among the radiations detected by this new sense, we may cite ultra-violet rays, X-rays, and the alpha, beta, and gamma rays from radioactive bodies.

conclusion

THE PHYSICIST IS DEFIED

In the swift advance of science, research forges boldly ahead at a number of strategic points, thrusting spearheads deep into unexplored fronts. While its energies are being expended in the reconnaissance of new terrain, there is little time for detailed exploration and consolidation of the conquered territory. Thus there remain a number of "pockets of resistance," which do not dim the glory of the general conquest but which must later be thoroughly mopped up. The more leisurely work which follows reduces certain of these fortresses—sometimes at the cost of considerable effort in experimental and theoretical research. Many an interesting phenomenon has thus been discovered and clarified in regions of science already well trodden but in which there still remained some islets of ignorance.

At times, however, these fortresses resist many assaults and persist for a long time in the midst of well-subdued territory. They are well known, but are seldom attacked anew, because "it would not pay." The veterans point them out to the novices in passing, merely to divert the beginners, rather than to suggest a re-examination of the phenomena in question. These abandoned areas of science, however, sometimes harbor clues—hidden maps, as it were—which lead to the conquest of important new territory. Many a time has scientific fortune smiled upon those workers whose skill and patience have extracted such secrets. It is precisely in this manner that cosmic rays were discovered. The historical sequence of researches, results, and hypotheses is very instructive, and it should be described in some detail.

The story begins at the end of the past century. The study of gaseous ionization, which has furnished one of the most powerful methods of analyzing atomic phenomena, had led physicists to attempt to realize the conditions under which this ionization would vanish. This is one of the standard tricks of the scientist: he tries to simplify the experimental conditions by first suppressing completely the phenomenon under examination and then reintroducing it gradually in a controlled manner. Thus, to study a gas he begins with a vacuum; to study light he must first create darkness.

The better to understand the process of ionization, therefore, physicists tried inclosing various gases in airtight containers, well protected from all known ionizing agents, such as gamma rays or X-rays. These gases, which would be perfect insulators if they contained no free electrical charges, nevertheless continued to behave like conductors. Invariably they remained feebly ionized, permitting a current to pass and slowly to discharge a sensitive electrometer. Naturally enough, the scientists at first suspected all kinds of possible sources of error. They spent much time looking for electrical leaks which might discharge the electrometers; they probed the possible causes of the ineradicable ionization: radioactive "contamination" of the walls and the gas, radiations from the surrounding bodies, etc. However, when the mysterious current persisted in the face of the greatest precautions, they finally abandoned the search and dismissed this ionization as "residual."

Certain investigators, however—J. Elster, H. F. Geitel, and then C. T. R. Wilson—turned their attention to these elusive phenomena. About 1900, Wilson announced that he was undertaking experiments which might decide whether the persistent ionization were not produced by rays yet unknown, analogous to X-rays or to cathode rays but of extraterrestrial origin and exceedingly penetrating. This was an extraordinary prophecy for the time and one which was not swiftly fulfilled. Abandoning the search, some investigators went so far as to speak of "spontaneous" ionization. This really amounts to the implicit assumption that the gaseous molecules, suffering a sort of interior fermentation, break up from time to time into negative and positive particles. But so-called "spontaneous" phenomena have not had much luck in science. This epithet is, in fact, merely an admission of impotence. A more penetrating analysis has finally dispelled the "spontaneity" in favor of a well-defined cause, arrived at as a result of scientific study. One needs only to recall how the "spontaneous-generation" theory was destroyed by Pasteur's discovery of microbes. In our own case the "spontaneous generation" was really due to a new radiation, the study of which was to throw a flood of light on some of the most burning problems in physics.

ENTER JULES VERNE

The problem would perhaps have remained long unsolved if several physicists had not possessed the spirit of adventure which was to play so great a role in the evolution of cosmic-ray research. We have said that the production of ions in a volume of gas inclosed in an ionization chamber is measured in ions per cubic centimeter per second. For normal air at sea-level, this number lies between ten and twenty. Protecting the ionization chamber by several centimeters of lead reduced it to about two, a decrease attributable to the absorption of radioactive rays from the ground. To ascertain how much of the residual ionization in the air is produced by rays emanating from the earth's crust, certain physicists decided to get away from the ground. For this purpose they carried their apparatus in free balloons up to considerable altitudes. Their instruments, consisting of a combination of ionization chamber and electroscope, measured at each instant the value of the "residual" ionization. As they ascended higher and higher, the physicists interposed between their apparatus and the ground an ever thicker stratum of air, up to an equivalent mass of about 50 cm. of lead. They naturally expected to observe a decrease in ionization due to the progressive weakening of the terrestrial rays by the atmospheric shield; from this rate of diminution they hoped to deduce the absorption coefficient, in air, of the radiation from the ground.

For the first few hundred yards of their ascent the investigators observed an appreciable decrease, in conformity with the predictions. But the diminution soon stopped, leaving a considerable residuum of ionization. Moreover, in certain high flights the trend actually reversed: following the initial decrease, it showed a noticeable increase. This was quite contrary to expectations, and it rendered untenable the hypothesis that the residual ionization of air is due to radioactive rays from the ground. One of the scientists who made these measurements, the Swiss investigator A. Gockel, found in 1909 that at $2\frac{1}{2}$ miles his electroscope discharged more rapidly than it did at the ground. In 1910 V. F. Hess, an Austrian physicist, attained an even higher altitude and found in the course of his ascent a very distinct increase in ionization. He advanced for the first time the hypothesis—substantially supported by his experiments—that the rays responsible for this increased ionization might be of extraterrestrial origin. Hess suggested that these "rays from on high" (*Höhenstrah-*

lung) might be rays of the same character as those from radio-active bodies but endowed with a penetrating power so much greater that they could traverse the entire atmosphere. As a matter of fact, the atmosphere is equivalent to about 3 feet of lead (if we take account only of the relative *masses* of air and lead)—at least ten times the maximum thickness which can be traversed by the most penetrating gamma rays. Finally, between 1911 and 1913 the German scientist W. Kolhörster rose still higher, reaching, at a height of about 6 miles, a region where the residual ionization is nearly thirty times greater than that observed on the ground. What was formerly a "residual effect" had thus become a significant phenomenon, the rapid development of which would no longer be delayed: cosmic rays had been discovered! Hess was subsequently awarded the Nobel Prize for his share in the discovery.

CHAPTER TWO

The Heroic Epoch

IN THE course of its history every science passes through one or more "heroic" epochs. After an early period of cautious gropings, investigators plunge with fervor into an exploration of the new terrain. In such a time the most improbable theories are apt to be verified, and those which appeared most substantial, discarded. In such a time, too, a few pioneers are hopeful of achieving the "hopeless" and envisage the ready solution of age-old problems. Then these sciences come of age; they become more widely known and studied, they proliferate and specialize; details now draw attention hitherto denied them in the rapid forward march. This is the classical age, the period of maturity. In due time comes an era of final accounting; the balance sheets are drawn up, the great treatises written. This is also a time in which one must be vigilant against the terrible enemy of progress: dogmatism.

After an interruption of nearly ten years, caused by the first World War, the studies of the "rays from the sky" were resumed in 1922; and they soon—between 1925 and 1935—reached their heroic epoch. We have seen that, according to Hess and Kolhörster, these rays have a very high penetrating power. This fact was verified in various ways, of which some were rather picturesque. The screens required for shielding against these new rays must be so thick that one would need to resort, for convenience, to the large bodies of matter found in nature. The masses of water in lakes and seas, the earth's crust, or the atmosphere provide screens as thick as one could desire. Thus, by a curious coincidence, the elements of the alchemist—earth, air, water—were subjected to the investigations of the modern physicist. Of the four "primary substances," only fire does not absorb cosmic rays!

MOUNTAINEERS, MINERS, DIVERS, AND FLIERS

The variety of environments in which these measurements have been made staggers the imagination. Here are a few curious examples: They have been investigated under heaps of marine salts in brine pits; under masses of urea; in the depths of a cannon of such large bore that one could put into it not only the apparatus but also the observer himself; in the catacombs of Paris; in coal, iron, and copper mines; in deep grottoes; in crevasses of glaciers; and on high mountain peaks. They have been measured in airplanes, in free balloons, and in stratospheric balloons; in the depths of lakes, in Norwegian fiords, and in the Red Sea; in all climates, longitudes, and latitudes.

The physicists who carried out these experiments had to be great sportsmen at times. As occasion demanded, they became divers, mountaineers, miners, or airmen. Even their apparatus had to be endowed with adventurous spirit in order to function under the strange conditions in which it was placed. Thus the "divers" put an ionization chamber or counters into a watertight caisson which could be lowered into a lake or ocean to a depth of many hundred yards. Inside this diving bell there was installed a complete little laboratory, with a source of energy consisting of dry cells and storage batteries—a sort of central electrical plant furnishing the different currents and voltages required. A camera permitted the registration, on a moving film, of the temperature and the indications of the various instrument dials. After an immersion of long duration the film was developed and the records examined.

The "mountaineers," among whose ranks the author of this book is enrolled, have constructed light and portable apparatus which can be readily installed in mountain shelters. Thus a cloud chamber built by P. Ehrenfest weighed no more than about 44 pounds, including the light-source and photographic equipment. This chamber was the first to yield pictures of cosmic-ray tracks at a high altitude (2 miles). Certain instruments, on the other hand, had to operate in the clefts of glaciers; and, in order to transform such crevasses into temporary laboratories, it was necessary to equip them with electrical power (Pl. I, A). (The plates are at the end of the book.)

The "miners" had to work in mine galleries with very low ceilings; they used little coal trucks to move their apparatus from place to place. Because the effects observed under great thicknesses of rock are very minute, the counters constructed for this purpose were large and cumbersome (more than a yard long). Moreover, the atmosphere was always so damp in these galleries that the instruments had to be inclosed in airtight containers.

Finally, there are the "airmen," who may be grouped into two classes: those who send their cosmic-ray detectors off into the stratosphere unaccompanied, and those—comprising only a handful—who dare to accompany them. Apparatus sent up alone must carry a self-contained "laboratory," similar to that of the submarine caissons, which automatically records the measurements. Or, instead, the little gondola may be converted into a miniature radio transmitting station which, throughout the flight, sends information about the intensity of the cosmic rays, the altitude, and the temperature. The experiments in manned balloon flights have captured the popular interest—notably the first flight of the stratospheric pioneer, Professor A. Piccard. His intrepidity and skilful technique have since been emulated by a series of brilliant successors.

Thanks to these experiments, curves showing the variation with altitude of the new radiations could be plotted; thus we now know the variation of the residual ionization as a function of the total thickness of air above the apparatus. It is convenient to represent this function by a curve (Fig. 4) whose ordinates are the values of I, the number of ions appearing per cubic centimeter per second, and whose abscissas are the thicknesses of the atmospheric screen in grams per square centimeter.[1] The figure so obtained represents the absorption curve of the rays in the atmosphere. A peculiarity of this curve which at once struck physicists is the slight bend in its ascending portion.

The very slow decrease in ionization with increasing thickness of screen shows the exceedingly high penetrating power of the new rays. This property appears all the more striking when compared with those of other radiations: ordinary X-rays are half absorbed by several millimeters of lead; gamma rays from the most penetrating radioactive substances known

[1] That is to say, the weight of a column of air one square centimeter in cross-section and equal in height to the screen thickness. For normal barometric pressure, the latter amounts to about 2 pounds.

can traverse a few centimeters of lead, several decimeters of water, or several hundred yards of air. The new rays traverse more than 3 feet of lead, or more than 30 feet of water, before their intensity is diminished by one-half; and their effect is still detectable under screens consisting of hundreds of

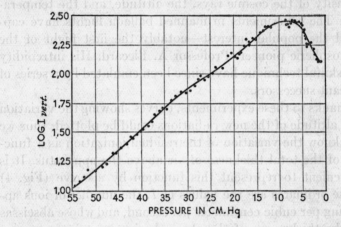

FIG. 4.—In this curve the logarithm of the total ionization, I, is plotted against the atmospheric pressure. The increase in I is very nearly an exponential function of the pressure (the semilogarithmic curve is approximately rectilinear). The exponential increase is followed by a maximum at about 10 cm. of mercury, after which the ionization decreases.

yards of water or even of rock. Such is their penetrating power that it is practically impossible completely to shield instruments from their effects, even by utilizing nature's enormously thick screens. Under mountains, in tunnels, in mines hundreds of feet deep, they can still be found and still be measured. In view of this, it is not surprising that the early attempts to protect electrometers against the source of residual ionization failed.

Among the most comprehensive measurements of the absorption of cosmic rays, we cite those of E. Regener and his school, which have made it possible to establish a continuous curve from the uppermost layers of the stratosphere (at an altitude of 18½ miles) down to a depth of 830 feet in water. The intensity of ionization at these two extreme positions varies by a factor of more than 10,000. R. A. Millikan and G. H. Cameron, as well as others, have obtained similar curves, so that the variation in total ionization due to the cosmic rays is now very well known all along their descent through the atmosphere and the water of lakes or oceans. Later we shall consider certain important details of these curves; for the moment, we turn our attention to their general characteristics.

Let us recall that electromagnetic rays are, in general, subject to an exponential absorption while traversing matter. This means that such rays are weakened in the same proportion in traversing each equivalent thickness of matter. One expresses this law by the equation $I_x = I_0 e^{-\mu x}$, where I_x is the intensity after traversing a thickness x of material, I_0 the initial intensity, e the Naperian base of logarithms, and μ the linear absorption coefficient characteristic of the material and of the rays in question. It is often customary to use a "mass absorption coefficient," μ/ρ, obtained if we divide μ by the density ρ of the material constituting the absorber. This coefficient is measured in "square centimeters per gram"; and it is then necessary to write $I_x = I_0 e^{-(\mu/\rho)(\rho x)}$, where ρx is the weight of a column 1 cm.² in cross-section in a screen x cm. thick and is measured in grams per square centimeter.

This law of absorption is followed by rays which do not suffer a change of properties in traversing matter; they decrease only in intensity. Other rays (e.g., alpha rays), which are subject to a continual alteration of their properties (slowing-down of the particles), show a very different type of absorption. From an analysis of atmospheric and aquatic curves, Regener, B. Gross, and G. Pfotzer considered it possible to detect a mixture of four classes of rays, of which the absorption coefficients have the following values: 8.5; 4; 1; 0.2 (in 10^{-2} cm.^{2} per gram). In any event, without going into such a detailed analysis, it is clear that a homogeneous radiation cannot give rise to such curves; a part of the rays is certainly very absorbable, or "soft," and another is extremely penetrating, or "hard." This last component can traverse as much as 10 feet of lead without losing one-half of its intensity; it is this portion which the "mining" physicists find in their subterranean depths.

Another interesting conclusion can be drawn by comparing the relative absorbing powers of different materials. The result is rather simple in the case of the hard radiation; in fact, the absorbing powers of different substances are much the same, if one takes into account the densities of the screens, i.e., that the coefficient, μ/ρ, defined above, is very nearly independent of the nature of the screen. For example, 1 cm. of lead is equivalent to 11 cm. of water or 4 cm. of aluminum. One often takes as the unit screen a layer of water 1 meter (3.28 feet) thick. This screen is roughly equivalent to 10 cm. of lead or 1 kilometer (3,280.8 feet) of air. Thus it has become customary to evaluate in meters of water the screen thickness which one interposes in the path of cosmic rays. The following are some typical cases: the thickness of atmosphere which the rays must pierce to reach apparatus at sea-level is equivalent to 10.3 meters of water (this is written $h = 10.3$ m. H$_2$O). It is 6.8 m. of water at the laboratory on the Jungfraujoch (3,500 m. above sea-level) and less than 0.1 m. of water at the highest altitudes attained by sounding balloons. At great depths under water or under ground, absorption by the atmosphere becomes almost negligible, and the screens are measured in hundreds of meters of water. Thus, in the coal and iron mines, J. Barnóthy and M. Forró have descended deeper than $h = 1,000$ m. H_2O in the course of their intensity measurements. The total variation of cosmic-ray intensity between these depths and the stratosphere is very considerable.

In attempting to account for the extraordinary penetrating power of the cosmic rays, we are confronted by the question: What is the nature of these radiations? The earliest hypotheses were suggested by analogy with the most penetrating rays known, i.e., those emanating from radioactive bodies. These rays are of three kinds:

1. The gamma rays, electromagnetic in character, which constitute the extreme short-wave extension of the optical spectrum;

2. The beta rays, which are electrons, i.e., charged particles; and

3. The alpha rays, very strongly absorbed by matter, which are not to be considered here.

The question then resolves itself as follows: Are the cosmic rays of the gamma type or of the beta type? Whichever they might be, one thing emerges clearly from the researches on their penetrating power: The new radiations must in any event carry the prefix "ultra"; they must be *ultra*-gamma rays or *ultra*-beta rays.

JULES VERNE AGAIN

Actually, we have long known of rays which might be called "cosmic" and which are of the gamma- or beta-ray type. Thus, for example, the sun sends us light (electromagnetic waves) as well as electrons. We also know that the intensity distributions of these various rays over the earth's surface are quite different, depending upon their nature. For example, light is propagated in straight lines, so that only the positions of the source and of material obstacles determine its direction, while electron beams are deviated by elec-

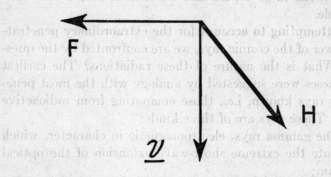

Fig. 5a.—Direction of the force (*toward the left*) acting on a positively charged electrical particle moving in the direction *v* in a magnetic field *H*.

tric and magnetic fields. An electrical particle in motion is, in fact, equivalent to an electric current and subject to the same electromagnetic effects. Thus, a positive particle in motion— for example, a proton—is equivalent to an electric current traveling in the same direction.[2] An electron in motion, on the other hand, constitutes a current moving in the opposite direction. Now we know that, when a current-carrying con-

[2] We might recall that the elementary particle known as the "electron" has a mass of 9.1×10^{-28} grams and a negative charge of 1.6×10^{-20} electromagnetic units. The proton, which is the nucleus of the hydrogen atom, is about two thousand times as massive, but it carries a positive charge equal in absolute value to that of the electron.

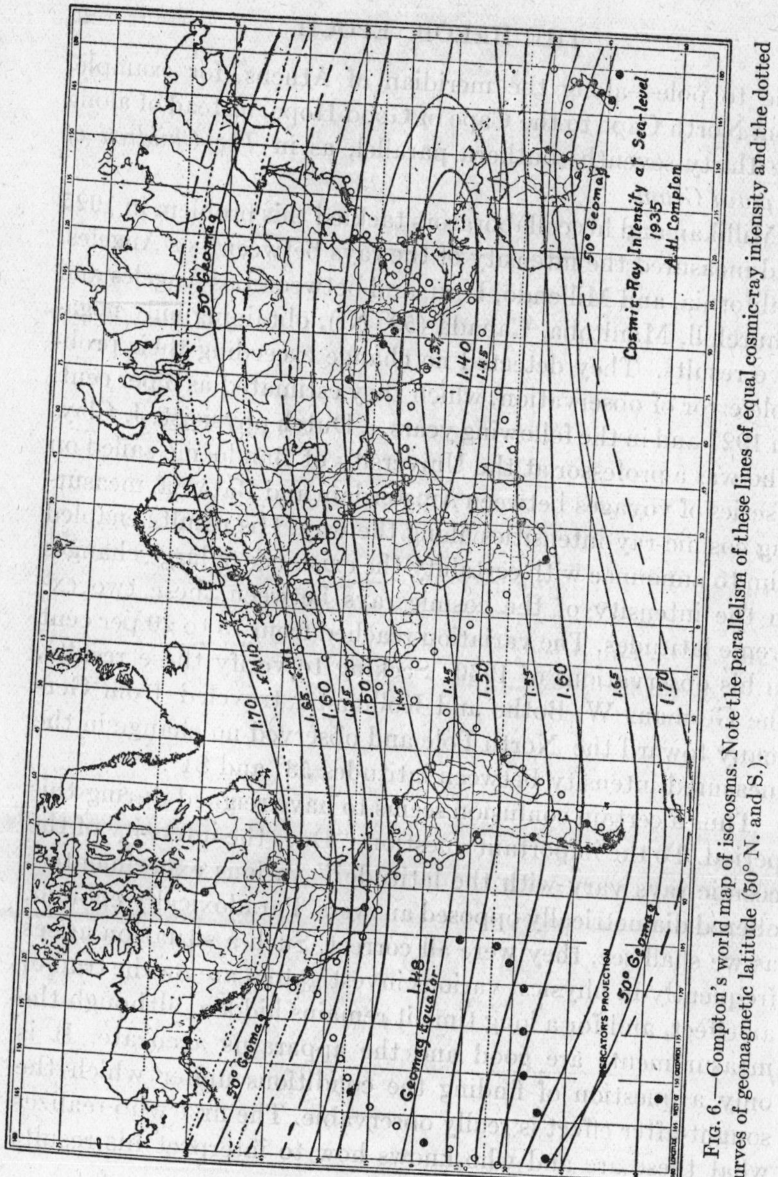

ductor is placed in a magnetic field, it is acted upon by a force directed at right angles to the current. The "three-finger rule," well known to Sophomore students of physics, gives the direction of this force: it is perpendicular both to the magnetic lines of force of the field and to the direction of mo-

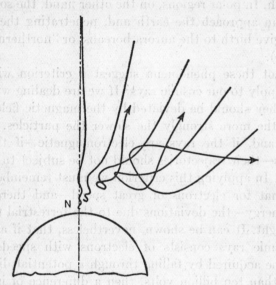

FIG. 5b.—Various trajectories of electrons in the earth's magnetic field. In the case of electrons with moderate energies, only those directed toward the polar regions can reach the earth.

tion (Fig. 5a). If the particles move vertically downward and the field is directed horizontally toward the reader, then positive particles are deviated toward the left and negative ones to the right. This phenomenon can be observed in a cathode-ray tube, in which the electrons travel in a well-defined beam, rendered visible by the luminescence of the gas. A magnet brought close to the tube deviates this beam as if it were a

FIG. 6.—Compton's world map of isocosms. Note the parallelism of these lines of equal cosmic-ray intensity and the dotted curves of geomagnetic latitude (50° N. and S.).

Cosmic-Ray Intensity at Sea-level
1935
A.H. Compton

current traveling in the opposite direction; and the particles, being free in a rarefied gas, describe circles. Now, the action of the earth's magnetic field on the electronic rays emitted by the sun is essentially to deviate those electrons which arrive in equatorial regions and prevent them from reaching the earth. In polar regions, on the other hand, the solar electrons can approach the earth and, penetrating the atmosphere, give birth to the aurora borealis, or "northern lights" (Fig. 5b).

Do not these phenomena suggest a criterion which we might apply to our cosmic rays? If we are dealing with electrons, they should be deviated by the magnetic field of the earth—the more strongly the slower the particles. On the other hand, if the rays are electromagnetic—if they are photons—their trajectories should not be subject to any deflection. In applying this criterion we must remember, however, that for electrons of great speed—and therefore of great energy—the deviations due to the terrestrial field are very slight. It can be shown, nevertheless, that if a part of the cosmic rays consists of electrons with speeds which would be acquired by falling through a potential difference of less than ten billion volts, then a difference of intensity should be discernible between polar and equatorial regions. The existence of such a variation would then make it certain that at least a part of the cosmic rays consists of charged particles of an electronic character.

Investigations leading to this conclusion could not be made without transporting cosmic-ray meters to widely scattered parts of the globe, at latitudes extending from the equator to the vicinity of the poles. The ideal itinerary would follow a magnetic meridian; and one can well imagine what a plot Jules Verne might have woven about an expedition from

pole to pole—along the meridian of Athens, for example, from North Cape to the Cape of Good Hope, instead of along the thirty-seventh southern parallel, as in *The Children of Captain Grant*.

Millikan and his collaborators tackled this problem in 1925 and measured the intensity of the rays between Los Angeles, California, and Millendo, Peru, and between Los Angeles and Churchill, Manitoba, Canada (59° N.), obtaining only negative results. They detected no change exceeding their probable error of observation, which they estimated as 6 per cent. In 1927 and in the following years, a Dutch physicist, J. Clay, who was a professor at the University of Bandoeng, sailed on a series of voyages between Amsterdam and Batavia, measuring cosmic-ray intensities along the way. His results enabled him to announce with certainty the existence of large changes in the intensity of the cosmic rays between these two extreme latitudes. The variation reached from 15 to 20 per cent in his observations of 1930. Seeking to verify these results, the Germans W. Bothe and Kolhörster traveled from Germany toward the North Pole and observed no change in the measured intensity between latitudes 53° and 81°.

Thus a certain confusion seems to have reigned during this period. To the important question, "Does the intensity of the cosmic rays vary with the latitude?" various experimenters offered diametrically opposed answers. Paradoxically enough, as we shall see, they were all correct. Such a situation arises frequently in physics: various investigators are on the trail of an effect, and for a long time it remains hidden, although the measurements are good and the apparatus accurate. It is only a question of finding the conditions under which the sought-after effect is really observable. The first who realizes what these are and who knows how to interpret his results

correctly is winner of the contest. In our case, we know today that Clay traveled along one of the most favorable paths for obtaining evidence for the magnetic effect; on the other hand, Bothe and Kolhörster had traversed a region of the globe where, as was later realized, the variations are—and should be—absolutely zero.

In a number of globe-circling voyages A. H. Compton, together with his collaborators, measured the cosmic-ray intensity along his journeys (Pl. II). As a result, he was able to draw a world map showing curves of equal cosmic-ray intensity, or "isocosms" (Fig. 6). It was then observed that it is possible to represent the variations of intensity as a function of the geomagnetic latitude in the following manner: There are two polar caps extending approximately to latitude 50°, over which the intensity does not vary appreciably. Everywhere in these regions $I = 1.8$. Between these caps lies an equatorial band on which the intensity is lower. A curve of minimum intensity runs near the middle of this band, following the Equator approximately. The isocosms, then, are curves analogous to parallels of latitude. However, it is the magnetic—not the geographic—latitude which is important in these phenomena; and if one compares the isocosms with magnetic parallels, one finds that these curves follow one another very closely—this is especially true of the geomagnetic equator and the isocosm of minimum intensity. Along a meridian from the north magnetic pole to the south magnetic pole the intensity-variation of the rays describes a peculiar curve (Fig. 7), resembling a basin with a wide rim. The polar plateaus represented by the rim meet the concave portion in a rather sharp angle. Moreover, the depth of this basin—i.e., the percentage intensity diminution in the equatorial band—is not the same for all longitudes but varies be-

tween 8 and 15 per cent. This arises from the circumstance
that the terrestrial magnetic dipole does not lie exactly at the
earth's center. One can understand how Bothe and Kolhörster, traversing one of the polar plateaus, did not observe any
variation. Millikan, traveling along the meridian on which
the variation is smallest, i.e., the west coast of America,
thought that the observed variation of several per cent could
be ascribed to experimental errors. Finally, Clay, having

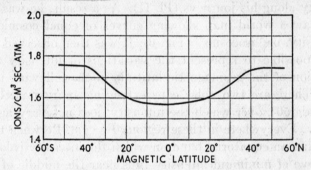

Fig. 7.—Clay's latitude curve, showing the equatorial depression in cosmic-ray
intensity, and the two polar plateaus. (After Clay.)

chosen just those longitudes along which the variation is the
greatest (in the Indian Ocean), found unambiguous evidence
for it (Fig. 7).

Today the variations with latitude of cosmic-ray ionization are well known, and they provide a conclusive argument
in favor of the corpuscular and electrically charged nature of
the primary cosmic radiation. The further to bolster this argument, however, it was desirable to investigate how the
number of cosmic-ray particles varies with geomagnetic latitude. To determine this number one must measure, instead
of the total ionization, the number n of penetrating particles
which strike a unit horizontal surface per minute. This can

be done with a system of Geiger-Müller counters. Such an apparatus, transported through various latitudes and functioning continuously during the voyage, enables one to trace a curve of minimum values of n as a function of geomagnetic latitude. The experiment was carried out by the author and L. Leprince-Ringuet aboard a steamship in the course of a round trip between Le Havre and Buenos Aires. Their measurements demonstrated that it is indeed the change in the number of particles which determines the equatorial "depression" in the latitude curve, their character being practically the same.

The corpuscular nature of at least a portion of the cosmic rays reaching the upper atmosphere has thus been demonstrated. Simultaneously, the extraterrestrial origin of the cosmic particles has also been proved for the following reason: Simple calculations show that the curvature of such a high-energy particle in the earth's magnetic field is too small to permit an appreciable deviation in the atmospheric portion of its trajectory. Hence the deviations leading to the geographic variations in intensity must be produced at considerable distances—say, of the order of the terrestrial radius—from the earth's surface.

A COSMIC RAINSTORM

A set of Geiger-Müller counters can be oriented in various ways to give precise information about the penetrating rays which discharge them. For example, let us arrange two of these counters with their axes horizontal, one above the other (Fig. 8). Then only those particles whose paths lie on or near the vertical plane through the axes can traverse both counters. It is then possible to connect the two counters in an electrical circuit capable of registering only their simultaneous discharges. When the apparatus records such an event, we say that it has indicated a "coincidence." The circuit is so designed that those particles or ionizing rays which create ions in only one of the counters are unable to set off the apparatus. One can see that this arrangement allows us to eliminate spurious effects—for example, the radioactivity of surrounding objects—which do not give rise to coincidences. Clearly, a coincidence might also be caused by two particles,

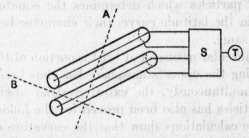

FIG. 8.—Arrangement of two counters for "vertical coincidences." Particle A gives rise to simultaneous electrical pulses in the two counters; and the selector, S, transmits an impulse to the adding meter, T. Particle B, which traverses only one of the counters, is not registered by the circuit.

one of which traverses one counter while the second simultaneously passes through the other. Since, however, the probability of occurrence of a single particle is much greater than the coinstantaneous passage of a pair of them, only the former case is of importance. The apparatus also acts as a geometric selector, as it registers only those particles which arrive from certain directions. It is frequently called a "telescope" for this reason.

With a coincidence-counting apparatus it is possible to measure accurately the number of cosmic-ray particles which traverse it. In this way it is found that at least one particle per minute strikes 1 cm.^{2} of horizontal surface (at sea-level).

These particles arrive at random, like raindrops in a storm; and the time intervals separating their arrivals have all possible values. Often, in listening through a loud-speaker[3] to the noise of this cosmic "hail," one gets a curious impression: at times it sounds like a tempest; then, again, the squall gives way to a lull. These illusions are, however, dispelled by a more extended statistical analysis.

At this point a question may be troubling you: Do these highly penetrating particles continually raining down upon us pass through our bodies? Indeed, they do; the surface which the human body presents to the cosmic shower is about 1 square foot; as a result, we are pierced from head to toe at a rate of more than twenty times per second by this subtle bombardment. Rest assured, however, that it produces no effect, either good or bad, on our bodily well-being; and, if some slight biological effects do spring from the cosmic rays, they are not detectable except through very specialized studies in genetics. Observe, moreover, that the inhabitants of a city like Quito, Ecuador, perched at a height exceeding 9,000 feet above sea-level, are struck by a "hail" about three times as dense as are we without suffering any damage. Conversely, miners, who during their work are amply sheltered against the rays, seem to be none the healthier for it.

FIRST INVENTORY

Let us pause for a breathing spell after all our excursions on land, on sea, and in the air and try to get our bearings.

We have been convinced that we are dealing with rays which originate outside of the earth's atmosphere, because

[3] The electrical impulse engendered by the passage of a cosmic-ray particle may be utilized to produce a discharge in a loud-speaker or to illuminate an indicator lamp; it is thus that one can "hear" or "see" the passage of the rays.

the higher we go, the greater becomes their intensity. This increase continues up to an altitude at which only one-twentieth of the atmosphere lies above the apparatus. The fact that these rays are bent by the earth's magnetic field requires that they travel long distances in this field in order to reach us and, consequently, that they come from regions at a distance of at least two terrestrial diameters. We also deduce from the deviations of their paths in the earth's magnetic field that the primary cosmic radiations consist of charged particles and not electromagnetic waves, or photons—at least, so far as most of them are concerned. Finally, the cosmic rays are absorbed by screens of matter in a way which suggests that at least two components of different hardness are present.

Another consequence of the earth's magnetic field has been predicted by Bruno Rossi, as well as by G. Lemaître and M. S. Vallarta. It results from the fact that electrical particles are deflected by a magnetic field in a direction perpendicular to the field and to their own motion, but in one sense or the other depending upon whether their electrical charge is positive or negative. Thus particles coming from extraterrestrial space and reaching the earth near the equator are deviated toward the east if they are charged positively; i.e., they seem to come from a westerly direction. If they are negative, the opposite is true. Should it happen that in the ensemble of particles moving toward the earth one of the electrical signs predominates, an asymmetry would be manifest in the distribution of rays from one side or another of the magnetic meridian.

In investigating the question of an east-west asymmetry, we again use coincidence counters. Two or three of these counters, their axes oriented horizontally and parallel to one another, determine a plane which contains the magnetic meridian if the axes of the counters point in the direction of the magnetic needle (Fig. 9a). We mount these counters on a support such that their plane can be inclined toward the east or west at varying angles—for example, between 15° E. and 15° W. At each orientation the number of coincidences per

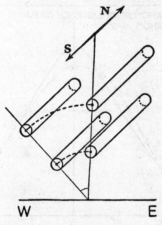

Fig. 9a.—Arrangement of counters for the study of east-west asymmetry

hour is plotted on a graph as ordinate, against the angle θ as abscissa. The resulting curve, which should have a maximum for the vertical ($\theta = 0$), shows, instead, a displaced maximum; i.e., it is asymmetric. Such experiments were performed by T. Johnson, by L. Alvarez and Compton, and by others, in regions near the equator. The number of particles seeming to arrive from the west being greater than that from the east, these workers concluded that a positive charge predominates among the cosmic-ray particles before their entry into the atmosphere. One can predict that this asymmetry should show a maximum at the magnetic equator and tend to zero in the regions of the polar plateaus. This effect was verified by Johnson as well as by the author and Leprince-Ringuet (Fig. 9b).

From observations on the effects of the earth's magnetic field, physicists have also been able to obtain some information about the kinetic energy of the charged particles which

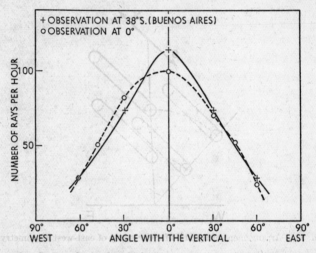

+ OBSERVATION AT 38°S. (BUENOS AIRES)
o OBSERVATION AT 0°

NUMBER OF RAYS PER HOUR

100

50

90°　60°　30°　0°　30°　60°　90°
WEST　　　ANGLE WITH THE VERTICAL　　　EAST

Fig. 9b.—Curves obtained with the counter arrangement in Fig. 9a at the geomagnetic equator and at latitude 30° S.

reach the upper atmosphere. We have said that the paths of such particles are curved in the earth's magnetic field. If we calculate the shape of these trajectories as did F. C. M. Störmer, followed by Lemaître and Vallarta, some very interesting conclusions can be drawn. One of the most important of these is the following: In order for an electron to be able to reach the surface of the earth at a certain latitude, its energy must exceed a certain minimum (particles with less energy are rejected toward infinity and cannot reach the ground or even the atmosphere). The minimum energy required depends upon the magnetic latitude and increases from the pole to the equator, going from 0 up to about 1.5×10^{10} ev.[4] At the pole, all particles can arrive, no matter how feeble their energy. At the equator, those with an energy below the extremely high value of 2×10^{10} ev. are rejected. Since about 90 per cent of the cosmic rays are able to reach the equator at sea-level, there must be a large proportion of particles with energy equal to or exceeding 1.5×10^{10} ev. in the primary cosmic radiation.

On the other hand, some interesting consequences follow from the particular shape of Clay's curve, which, as will be recalled, resembles a sort of basin with a flat rim. Let us travel with our apparatus from the equator toward either pole. At the equator there arrive all cosmic-ray particles with an energy greater than 2×10^{10} ev. The farther we advance toward the pole, the lower this limit descends; as we receive particles of lower and lower energy along with the faster ones, we observe an increase in the total number. At a latitude of $40°$, however, where the limiting energy is 6×10^9 ev., a change sets in; in this region the number of cosmic-ray particles stops increasing. What is happening here? Is there something preventing the particles of still lower energy from reaching the ground, or may it perhaps be that there are no such particles in the primary radiation? It is natural, offhand, to seize upon the first hypothesis, since one might suppose that the atmosphere prevents particles of very low energy from reaching the ground. We shall soon see, however, that the second hypothesis is the correct one.

[4] We shall always evaluate the energy of particles in "electron-volts," written "ev." An electron-volt is the energy acquired by an electron when it is accelerated by a potential difference of 1 volt.

The various measurements described thus far have yielded certain basic information about the primary cosmic rays—for example, that they consist of electrical particles, mostly positive, moving with speeds so great that their energies may exceed 1.5×10^{10} ev. Apart from these several points, the rest of the subject is still shrouded in impenetrable fog.

QUESTION NO. 1 REMAINS UNANSWERED

Can we, in the light of this basic knowledge, try to answer Question No. 1, which has baffled physicists from the start? Even when they had known nothing more than the phenomenon of residual ionization, they had asked: "What is the origin of the rays which produce it?" We already know a part of the answer: "Their origin is extraterrestrial"; and this justifies the name "cosmic rays." However, by what processes can we imagine the particles to have attained their high energies? Let us remember that in order to reach the equator an electron must have a speed which would be imparted to it by an electrical field of 1.5×10^{10} ev. Even the fastest electrons emitted by radioactive bodies do not have one thousandth of this energy!

When the early period of cosmic-ray research ended, there was scarcely a plausible hypothesis as to their mode of origin, except one due to Millikan. This scientist noticed that, according to Einstein's relativistic conception of the universe, mass and energy are not absolutely distinct categories. They are, rather, similar entities, transmutable one into the other: thus, the destruction of a proton liberates a billion electron-volts. Let us suppose, then, that under certain conditions atoms with an atomic weight of approximately 20 may be subject to total destruction, the charges of electrons and protons neutralizing one another. If the equivalent energy of the disappearing masses be imparted to an electron pair, there may result a production of corpuscular rays possessing the required 10^{10} ev. What is the possibility of such a transformation? We shall have occasion to return to this question later; for the moment, let us merely acknowledge that Millikan's hypothesis was very attractive.

Moreover, whatever may be their mode of production, can we assign a place of origin to the cosmic particles? If the cosmic radiation originates in certain celestial bodies or certain regions of the sky, we should be able to determine this fact by studying the intensity variations of the radiation as a function of time, solar or sidereal. These investigations should show whether the intensity depends upon the presence of certain constellations or heavenly bodies above the horizon—and especially near the zenith. Such studies of time variations have been made repeatedly without hitherto revealing any marked changes.[5] In particular, neither the position of the sun nor that of the Milky Way appears to play any role. We may conclude that the cosmic rays do not originate in the sun or in any group of stars like the Milky Way. What, then, shall we suppose? Do they come from the nebulae? From the novae? From double stars? We shall perhaps be in a better position to solve this problem after having pushed further our investigations into the nature of the cosmic rays and their effects upon matter. Let us, then, temporarily put aside this Question No. 1, promising ourselves, however, to return to it later.

[5] Although some very feeble diurnal and seasonal modifications have been detected, these can mostly be interpreted as secondary effects due to changes in the atmosphere.

CHAPTER THREE

Showers, Pairs, Bursts, Stars

IN 1928, D. Skobelzyn, the first physicist to photograph the tracks of cosmic rays by the cloud-chamber method, observed that they tend to appear in groups. On single pictures he frequently found two or three tracks—proof that several particles had simultaneously traversed the apparatus along closely neighboring paths.

THE COSMIC RAYS ARE PROLIFIC

Examining these tracks more carefully, he deduced that the particles responsible for them must have been produced in regions close to the apparatus, particularly the ceiling and walls. He was unable to ascertain, however, whether they originated in a well-defined point. In collaboration with the author he attributed the production of these particles to the successive secondary effects of a very energetic ray. According to this view, the observed groups of tracks are made by "knock-on" electrons or by Compton electrons.[1] The frequent occurrence of such groups, which should accompany

[1] An energetic particle, colliding violently with the electrons of the material it traverses, sets them into rapid motion, thus forming ionizing rays: these are the "knock-on" electrons. In the Compton effect a photon suffers elastic collisions with the electrons it encounters; the latter acquire enough energy in the process to become ionizing particles.

the primary ray, proves that cosmic rays tend to multiply by producing secondaries in their passage through matter. Soon afterward, Rossi, utilizing cosmic-ray counters, discovered the great importance of these multiple secondary effects.

A striking consequence of the abundant production of secondary rays is the appearance of "transition effects." These may be explained as follows: Suppose we have an apparatus with which to measure the intensity of a bundle of energetic rays (gamma rays, for example). If we interpose a screen between the source and the apparatus—*above* the apparatus in the case of cosmic rays—we ordinarily observe a diminution of the indicated intensity. This means that some of the rays have been absorbed. Under certain conditions, however (e.g., when the absorbing screen is composed of an element of high atomic weight), the readings of our instruments show an initial rise. Of course, no new energy has been created in the screens; the apparent increase in intensity is due to a transformation of the initial radiation into a kind which acts more effectively on the measuring apparatus. Thus an electron entering a dense material generates numerous low-energy secondaries—electrons as well as photons. The secondary electrons ionize abundantly, while the secondary photons give rise to tertiary ionizing electrons (Pl. III).

These transition effects are very sensitive to the passage of cosmic rays from a medium of low density and small atomic weight into a dense substance consisting of heavy elements. E. G. Steinke has shown that lead plates, several millimeters thick, placed above an ionizing chamber augment the "residual ionization," i.e., the effect of the cosmic rays. It is the multiplication of the primary particles in the screen that is responsible for this effect. Electrons of higher energies produce much the same ionizations, regardless of their energy. Thus, if a particle of high energy, passing from air to lead, produces ten secondaries of low energy, the resulting ionization is ten times as strong. This effect can be seen in the curves of Figure 10: the first layers of lead give rise to a marked increase in ionization; then absorption predominates.

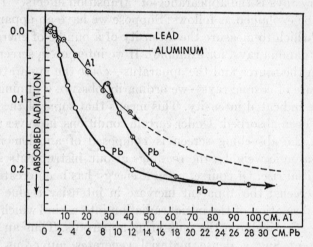

FIG. 10.—Transition effects produced by placing lead plates above an ionization chamber. It can be seen that the addition of layers of lead results at first in an increase in the effect of the cosmic rays, provided that there is no absorber of low atomic weight above the chamber. (After Steinke.)

The ionization chamber is not, however, an ideal apparatus for studying these secondary effects. Counters, and particularly "coincidence counters," are admirably suited to this purpose, as first demonstrated by Rossi. It must be admitted that this method has sometimes been used rather indiscriminately, and the reasons are not far to seek. Sets of counters lend themselves to an almost infinite variety of arrangement, and this flexibility has been exploited in constructing apparatus sensitive to larger or smaller groups of particles. However, different investigators, intending to measure the same thing, have by no means used the same experimental arrangements. Moreover, the dimensions of screens and counters, as well as their orientation,[2] vary with the observer. To be sure, the choice of these arrangements

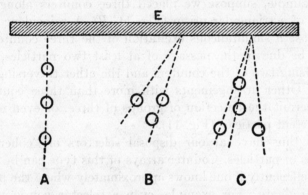

Fig. 11.—Coincidence selectors of three or four counters, sensitive to single particles (A) or to simultaneous groups of two or three particles (B, C) coming from the absorber, E.

has often conformed to certain "styles"; but these, as the literature discloses, were rather temporary and local. It is not surprising, therefore, that the results of various workers have not always been concordant.

Let us examine at this point several arrangements of counters which have been used in studying cosmic rays. First, consider two or more counter tubes in the same plane and parallel to each other—a so-called "counter telescope." Any particle passing through them generates in the several

[2] These are often referred to as the "geometry" of the assembly.

counters electrical discharges which are combined by a coincidence circuit[3] (Fig. 11, *A*). The apparatus counts only traversals of all the counters; it does not register isolated discharges. This arrangement enables us to select single particles moving in a given plane.

On the other hand, suppose we oriented these counters in such a way that a straight line cannot cross them all at once; for example, suppose we placed three counters along the edges of a triangular prism (Fig. 11, *B*). A coincidence—in this case a simultaneous excitation of the three counters— must be due to the passage of at least two particles, one traversing two of the counters and the other traversing the third. Other arrangements with more than three counters will permit the detection of groups of three, or even more, concurrent particles (Fig. 11).

We thus have at our disposal selectors of "coherent" groups of particles. Counter arrays of this type can be used more efficiently if one knows approximately where the particles originate. For example, even a selector consisting of only two counters can be made sensitive to groups of at least two rays. It suffices to orient the counters so that a single particle emerging from the point of origin cannot traverse them both. Similarly, a system of four counters, arranged along the edges of an equilateral triangular prism and along its axis, is sensitive only to groups of at least three particles whose paths do not intersect inside the prism (Fig. 11, *C*).

In studying larger groups of particles, it is hardly possible further to increase the number of counters. It becomes necessary, rather, to resort to the measurement of the ionization they produce along their paths. If, for example, a single electron produces 10,000 ions in traversing an ionization cham-

[3] See pp. 29–30.

ber and if the associated electrometer circuit is sensitive only to electrical impulses equivalent to more than 200,000 ions, then only groups of more than 20 particles will be detected with such an arrangement. It should be understood that these figures do not refer to an ordinary ionization apparatus; the number of ions cited is too small to be detected by an ordinary electrometer alone. Fortunately, the physicist possesses amplifying devices so powerful that, beginning with an exceedingly minute impulse (such as a discharge of a few thousand ions), he can obtain an electrical signal which may be registered and measured with an oscillograph. By suitably regulating the apparatus, one can classify the sets of particles detected according to their multiplicity; for example, groups of 20 electrons constitute one such category. Finally, we shall see later that certain very large groups require special investigation.

Let us try to analyze more closely the process of multiplication in the screens. Following Rossi's method, we place some slabs of lead above an apparatus which can select groups of two rays or more—as, for example, arrangement *B* of Figure 11. Increasing the thickness of these plates, millimeter by millimeter, from 0 to 10 cm., we measure for each thickness the number of groups of at least two rays which set off the apparatus in an hour (Fig. 12). Interposing the first few millimeters of lead, far from decreasing the number of cosmic rays, increases it considerably. Under favorable conditions we can detect this increase directly in several minutes by observing the average counting rate. The latter continues to rise as the screen keeps getting thicker, up to about 1.5–2.0 cm. of lead; and it may become as large as fifty times the rate without a screen. Then, if we add further layers of lead, a decrease sets in, which continues to about 5 cm. Finally, the curve almost levels off; beyond this point additional layers of lead produce only an extremely slow decrease.

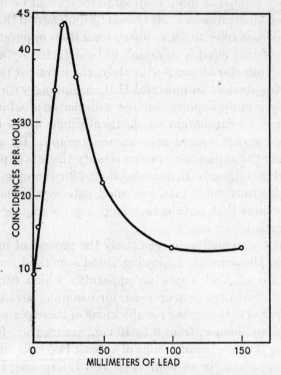

FIG. 12.—Shower curve (also called the "Rossi curve") obtained at an altitude of about 2 miles with an arrangement of four counters (see Fig. 11, *C*). Note the great increase resulting from the superposition of the first 2 cm. of lead, and the sharp maximum, followed by a gradually sloping decline.

This curve can be explained if we suppose that a multiplication[4] of cosmic rays can take place in a metallic plate. According to this hypothesis, a particle incident upon a lead

[4] Presently we shall discuss the nature of this multiplication.

plate several millimeters thick has a good chance of producing in it many secondary electrons capable of exciting a set of counters; the greater the thickness, the more secondaries will be created—up to about 2 cm. As these particles travel through the lead, some of them are stopped; but in the first 2 cm. the rate of multiplication exceeds the rate of absorption. Beyond that thickness, however, absorption gains the upper hand (certain of the primary particles as well as their secondaries can no longer leave the lead), and the curve descends. It is interesting to note that we should expect the curve to fall back to zero when the screen is sufficiently thick to absorb all the electrons; we shall see, in fact, that no electron of the incident radiation can traverse more than 15 cm. of lead. However, the curve does not continue to drop; instead, it levels off above zero. Therefore, a new explanation must be found for this "residuum."

We digress to point out again a remarkable feature which often characterizes the interpretation of experiments: a hypothesis is put forward which explains a phenomenon satisfactorily except for one or two obscure particulars. Later, these details—which had provisionally been labeled "residual"—serve as a point of departure for a new stride forward. This has proved true of the residuum mentioned above. It cannot be accounted for by the multiplication hypothesis. However, as we shall see in the next chapter, it was one of the links in a chain of reasoning which led to an important discovery.

The curve we have described is named after Rossi, the Italian physicist who was the first to carry out these striking experiments. Subsequently, the technique of coincidence-counting has been highly perfected by many investigators. Some tried also to photograph the paths of groups of particles with the Wilson chamber. To do this, considerable difficulties had to be surmounted. Thus, if one lets a cloud chamber function at random, as did Skobelzyn, it is only rarely (about once in twenty pictures) that an expansion coincides with the passage of a cosmic ray, and very seldom, indeed, with that of a group of particles. The yield is therefore rather poor; and the waste of time, photographic plates, and other equipment makes this kind of work unprofitable.

Certain physicists, among them G. L. Locher, of the United States, then tried to increase the number of useful pictures by photographing only expansions accompanied by events of interest. To accomplish this, Locher controlled the illuminating flash which furnished light for the picture by a pair of coincidence counters placed above and below the apparatus. As in the earlier apparatus, expansions were uncontrolled; i.e., an expansion might yield a cosmic-ray track or it might not. However, pictures were now taken only during expansions accompanied by the passage of a cosmic ray. A particle traversing the two counters—and therefore the chamber—while the gas was sensitive to ionization produced a coincident discharge; the latter set off a mechanism which flashed a light and took the picture. Even this ingenious apparatus, however, produced an inadequate yield; for, while few films were wasted, expansions were still initiated at random, and these seldom furnished good pictures of cosmic ray tracks.

Finally, the problem was solved by P. M. S. Blackett and G. P. S. Occhialini, who constructed a cloud chamber in which the expansion itself was controlled by the passage of an ionizing particle through two counters, placed above and below the chamber. In building such an apparatus, one is confronted with the difficulty that expansion does not occur until the cosmic-ray particle has passed through the chamber. In other words, the particle traverses a saturated gas insensitive to ions. Fortunately, however, the ions can persist for a fraction of a second without suffering too much recombination or diffusion. Hence, if the expansion and the accompanying supersaturation are produced soon enough after the passage of the electron, moisture condenses on the ions, delineating the path of the particle. Blackett constructed a high-speed apparatus, the moving parts of which were so light in weight that the expansion was produced within one one-hundredth of a second after the passage of the particle; tracks so produced are clear and undistorted. In this way he could rapidly obtain a large number of useful photographs, showing isolated particles a well as the doublets or triplets of Skobelzyn.

Moreover, Blackett was soon able to announce the existence of a new and very remarkable effect—a "beautiful phenomenon," by the standards of a physicist: in certain pictures he found volleys or clusters of dozens of electrons traversing together the gas of the cloud chamber. He observed also that these groups originate in points very close to the expansion chamber—e.g., the supports of the photographic apparatus or the various accessory equipment. He found, in fact, that the very walls of the chamber often serve as a source. The better to study these multiple phenomena, various physicists tried placing underneath the apparatus a selector set of the Rossi type with which to control the expansion. Blackett proposed that these groups of simultaneous cosmic-ray particles be called "showers."[5]

The pictures taken, thanks to these methods (e.g., Pl. IV),

[5] An apt name in rainy England! In agricultural and sunny France, they are called "sheaves."

revealed the real character of these groups whose existence had been proved by counter experiments. Showers are aggregations of more or less numerous secondary particles which are ejected from matter under the influence of the passage of cosmic rays and which are propagated in approximately the same directions as those of the initial particles. It is strange to reflect that such showers continually originate within our own body. We have seen that we receive about one thousand cosmic particles a minute, and in this interval of time hundreds of showers are created in the midst of our tissues without our being the least bit aware of it.

POSITRONS AND NEGATRONS: A STUDY IN SUBATOMIC SYMMETRY

Having succeeded in photographing the tracks of cosmic rays, physicists next tried to determine their energies. To this end, they utilized the action of a magnetic field. We have already examined the effects upon cosmic rays of the earth's magnetic field. These effects can be simulated in the laboratory by means of an electromagnet having a field strength of about 1,000 gauss. Moreover, the track of an electrical particle moving in this field can be made visible if we place a Wilson chamber between the poles of the magnet. Our particle moves in a circle under the action of the electromagnetic forces and of its own inertia. This circle is described clockwise for an observer looking along the direction and in the sense of the magnetic lines of force in the case of a negative corpuscle. From the radius of the circle we can deduce the kinetic energy of the particle if we know its charge and mass.

This method has proved extraordinarily fruitful in many domains of corpuscular physics. One of the first to apply it was P. L. Kapitza, a Russian physicist, who used it to study alpha rays. Skobelzyn employed the method in his researches on Compton electrons, in the course of which he observed the first visible tracks of cosmic rays. C. D. Anderson took pictures of single cosmic-ray particles traversing lead plates. Finally, in its counter-controlled form, the magnetic Wilson chamber enabled Blackett and Occhialini, then Anderson, J. C. Street, and many others, to get magnificent pictures of showers with branches curved by the field (Pl. V).

We shall soon examine the results furnished by these experiments regarding the energies of cosmic rays. First, however, let us notice that whether a particle is to be deflected in a clockwise or counterclockwise sense by the magnetic field depends upon the sign of its charge. Thus, for a negative cosmic ray proceeding from the atmosphere downward through the cloud chamber, we should expect a curvature of the kind described above. To their astonishment, Anderson and then Blackett and Occhialini got many pictures in which the particles were deviated in the opposite sense. If the particles in question are electrons with negative charge, one must assume that they travel upward from below, and consequently are not "direct" cosmic rays but reflected or secondary rays. Unfortunately for this hypothesis, the number of such tracks was much too high, being practically equal to the number of particles which traveled clockwise. Soon, moreover, a crucial experiment demonstrated that the particles in question were really traveling downward: a metallic plate was placed horizontally inside the cloud chamber. In crossing this plate a cosmic ray particle would lose a part of its energy; and, if it were moving downward, its energy below the plate would be less than that above. Anderson found this to be the case, even for counterclockwise tracks. These particles, therefore, must have come from above; and the sense of their curvature in the magnetic field left no doubt as to their charge: they were positive (Pl. VI). (The second cosmic-ray Nobel Prize was won by Anderson for this discovery.)

To avoid too risky a hypothesis, Anderson supposed at first that he was dealing with protons, for these were the lightest positive particles then known. But the density of ionization along the tracks did not permit him to retain this hypothesis very long. Moreover, Blackett was soon able to show that, if one photographs a shower in a magnetic field, approximately half the tracks go to the right and the other half to the left, their appearance being otherwise identical (Pl. V). A single explanation thus remained possible: the tracks showing anomalous deviation must be due to a new particle, having the mass and charge of the electron but opposite electrical sign. To this positive electron Anderson gave the name "positron"; to emphasize the distinction in sign, the ordinary electron is sometimes called "negatron." Thus we have two kinds of electrons: positrons and negatrons.

This was one of the great discoveries of modern physics. The appearance of this new particle re-established, to a certain extent, a balance which satisfies our instinctive feeling for symmetry. Many physicists had been struck with the great disparity between the two elementary electrical particles, the negative particle (electron) and the positive one (proton) being extremely different from one another. On the other hand, the positive electron and the negative one differ from one another only in the sign of their charge. Moreover, apart from this Pythagorean satisfaction, the simultaneous creation of two kinds of electricity, an old theory of early nineteenth-century physicists, found its most perfect expression in the appearance of the positron.

In order to investigate how these new particles come into being, one must first study a very remarkable phenomenon, the "materialization" of radiation. An alternative name for this process might be the "electronization" of photons, for it consists essentially in the transformation of a photon of high energy into a pair of oppositely charged electrons (i.e., a positron-negatron pair). This effect, first observed in photons of the cosmic rays, soon manifested itself also in the case of gamma rays from radioactive nuclei. It should be considered a general property of electromagnetic rays of very short wave-length or, more precisely, of photons with energies extending beyond a million electron-volts.

We have encountered several new phenomena all at once. The better to get our bearings, let us first go back to see how these effects can be explained in terms of our fundamental principles. The physicist is, in fact, governed by time-tested principles and laws. Provided one promises to respect these, he is ready to consider the strangest hypotheses, for he feels that he stands on solid ground. Let us then, at this point, briefly review several basic principles.

We cite first the principle of conservation of energy, which now embraces that of the conservation of matter, in consequence of Einstein's demonstration that mass and energy are equivalent; then the principle of conservation of momentum or impulse; finally, the principle of the conservation of electrical charge, which evidently plays an essential role here. Let us begin with the latter. This principle requires that the total charge of a system does not change, if one adds algebraically the positive and negative charges. Consequently, a neutral electrical system such as a photon cannot give birth to an electron alone but only to a number of electron *pairs*. The group of particles thus formed, having an equal number of positive and negative signs, constitutes a neutral electrical system. In short, the creation by a photon of a positron-negatron pair is permitted by the principle.

Let us now recall the first principle of thermodynamics: it requires that the total energy be conserved. Thus the energy of the photon must equal that of the two electrons to which it has given rise. Let us be careful, however, to use the principle of conservation of energy in its general sense, which includes the mass.[6] Each electron has a mass of 10^{-27} grams, which represents an energy of 5×10^5 ev. Hence, in creating a pair, it is necessary to expend 10^6 ev. merely in order to build up their mass in some manner. The minimum energy which a photon must possess to be materialized is then 10^6 ev. This explains why the phenomenon had so long escaped observation in the gamma rays of radioactive bodies, for the energies of these rays rarely exceed 10^6 ev. What happens to the extra energy if the photon has appreciably more than the minimum? It is imparted to the two electrons, projecting them into space and thus making them ionizing rays (Pl. VII). This enables us to detect them by the methods described at the beginning of this book.

Having satisfied the principles of conservation of electricity and of energy, we are confronted with two rapidly moving electrons in place of the initial photon. The principle of conservation of momentum, or impulse, must also be satisfied; i.e., it is necessary that the impulse of the photon $(h\nu/c)$,[7]

---

[6] As shown by Einstein, a mass m is equivalent to a quantity of energy mc^2, c being the speed of light. Conversely, the mass corresponding to an energy E is given by E/c^2.

[7] The total energy of a photon is equal to its frequency ν, multiplied by Planck's constant, h. This leads to a momentum of $h\nu/c$, c being the speed of the photon, i.e., the speed of light.

along its direction of propagation, be preserved in the momenta of the particles created or set in motion. One can show that this condition cannot be satisfied merely by choosing suitable directions for the trajectories of the pair. It is necessary that a third particle intervene, and this function is performed by an electron or nucleus in the material traversed by the photon. The sum of the momenta of these three particles may then be set equal to the initial momentum of the photon.

There is another way of showing why the production of pairs in a vacuum is impossible. As we have seen, there is a minimum energy (10^6 ev.) which a photon must have in order that it may create a pair; corresponding to this energy, E, there is a minimum frequency, ν, given by Planck's equation, $h\nu = E$. But we know that, if an observer is in motion with respect to the source of photons, the observed frequency is changed by the Doppler effect. Then, for a definite material "observer," it can be stated that the photon does or does not possess the minimum energy. If the materialization is to take place, therefore, it is necessary that in the neighborhood of the photon there should be an atom defining the system of reference with respect to which the photon has a sufficiently high frequency. In fact, it is in passing near a nucleus, i.e., through the latter's field, that the photon is subject to materialization. This explains why the cosmic rays can create pairs only in traversing matter and why this phenomenon occurs more readily in dense materials.

All that is born dies. The electrons and positrons should then, by a process inverse to that of their creation, be able to disappear as electrical charges. Let us apply our principles anew: For the conservation of electricity it suffices that each time a negatron disappears a positron also disappears. In other words, when a negatron encounters a positron, they fuse, neutralizing one another and leaving a charge of zero. The energy represented by the mass of the two electrons (10^6 ev.) plus their energy of motion becomes electromagnetic in form; consequently, one or more photons are formed, in accordance with the principle of conservation of energy. Suppose that the two electrons, prior to their fusion, are slow or practically motionless with respect to some system of reference. After fusion, then, the center of gravity of the system must move slowly, if the principle of conservation of momentum is to be satisfied. Therefore, it is necessary that two equal photons be emitted in opposite directions, with a frequency such that the energy of each is equivalent to 5×10^5 ev.

Even modern science, for all its precision and complexity, is not without its poetry. Picture this twin birth of oppositely charged electrons—swift and lusty—when an energetic photon of light brushes too close to an atom of matter. And picture, too, their twin death when, old and sluggish, they meet and fuse into one another, emitting, as they die, two identical wisps of light which fly off into space carrying their immortal souls of energy.

In any event, these processes satisfy our predilection for symmetry by putting the positive and the negative on an equal plane. However, since this symmetry exists, why are there not as many positrons as negatrons? Why is the positron so rare that its discovery waited until quite recently? Why is it so fleeting that, as soon as it loses the enormous speed which enables it to elude the influence of neighboring charges, it finds a mate and disappears? In an inverted universe in which atomic nuclei would be negative and electrons positive, we would probably observe rare and fleeting negatrons—and nothing would distinguish such a universe from our own. One must, however, take things as they are. Our universe is decidedly one of positive nuclei, and consequently one of negative electrons. Thus the asymmetry cannot be completely dissolved. Perhaps, however, we should rejoice in this circumstance, for a universe perfectly symmetrical in the two electricities would disappear immediately in a great burst of light.

In a free state or vacuum, positrons, like negative electrons, last indefinitely; and there is nothing to prevent them from constituting—at least partially—the primary cosmic particles which reach the top of our atmosphere and which are principally positive.

The series of phenomena we have been describing was later found experimentally in the domain of the higher-frequency radiations from radioactive bodies. It serves admirably to clarify the mechanism of shower production. However, before returning to the theory of showers, let us recapitulate these effects:

1. An electron of either sign, racing through matter, may, in traversing the very intense field near a nucleus, be suddenly slowed down. The retardation, liberating a part of its kinetic energy, permits the electron to emit this energy in the form of an electromagnetic photon. This is the "braking radiation," more commonly known under the German name "*Bremsstrahlung*," which physicists had previously encountered in the emission of continuous radiation from the targets of X-ray tubes.

2. An inverse phenomenon may occur in which a photon of very high frequency, passing through the field of a nucleus, disappears, giving birth to two electrons which form a positron-negatron pair. These electrons carry an energy such that the sum of their masses (computed as equivalent energy)

and their kinetic energy equals the energy lost by the photon (Pl. VII).

3. Finally, a slow positron, passing very close to an electron, may fuse with it, producing two photons. Their frequency is determined by their energy, and the latter is equivalent to the mass energies plus the kinetic energies of the two disappearing electrons.

Quantitatively, we note that an electron has a mass equivalent to 5×10^5 ev. Thus, as we have seen, process No. 2 cannot take place unless the photon's energy exceeds 10^6 ev. The excess energy goes to the newly created electrons, in a kinetic form. Process No. 3 gives rise to the creation of photons with 5×10^5 ev., since two photons replace each pair of disappearing electrons.[8]

Taken together, these effects of *Bremsung* and of creation, occurring as they do in rapid succession, provide a simple interpretation of the production of showers: An electron traversing matter is decelerated and gives rise to photons; these create pairs; each electron of these pairs, decelerated in turn, produces photons which create new pairs; and this continues as long as the energy carried by each particle remains greater than 10^6 ev. The avalanche built up in this fashion forms a shower. All particles possessing less than 10^6 ev. leave the picture, the positrons disappearing by fusion with negatrons, while the negative electrons become attached to ions or to neutral atoms. The photons are diffused by the Compton effect, and their career is finally ended by photoelectric absorption.

[8] We have, to be sure, oversimplified somewhat. For example, we have neglected the role of electrons in the direct creation of pairs by *Bremsung* (a German term commonly used by physicists for the deceleration which gives rise to electromagnetic radiation), as well as the role which they can play as the retarding bodies.

Showers have been studied in great detail with the counter technique as well as with the cloud chamber. For example, an expansion chamber constructed of light materials, with a partition composed of a heavy metal plate (in which practically all the showers are produced), has been used to obtain photographs of showers (Pls. III, IV, VII–XI) which supply convincing evidence for the various processes we have described. These pictures show the production of a pair started by a photon (Pl. VII), of a small shower started by an electron or a photon (Pls. VIII–X), and finally of larger showers starting with these components (Pls. III, IV, and XI). With two metallic plates, it has been demonstrated that shower particles which still possess enough energy are themselves capable of generating new showers, while electrons of meager energy are stopped. The energetic rays extend nearly in the direction of the initial particle, while the low-energy rays tend to diverge at larger angles from the "core" of the shower. Statistics show that the average angle of divergence is about 20°. Some of the photographs of showers obtained in this way are among the most beautiful and striking records in the field of modern physics.

It is reasonable to suppose that the process of shower formation depends on the kind of material in which the showers are generated by the cosmic rays. Comparisons of the shower-producing effects in screens of various thicknesses and composed of different elements have yielded significant results. Earlier studies on the absorption of penetrating corpuscular rays had shown that two metallic plates or screens are equally good absorbers if they have the same surface density (mass per square centimeter of surface). Now it was found that this criterion does not apply in comparing the efficacy of two screens as shower-producers, but rather that shower formation depends upon the atomic weight, or, even better, upon the atomic number of the element in question. Thus, 4 mm. of lead have a shower-producing power equivalent to that of 3 cm. of aluminum or of 30 cm. of water, while the corresponding density equivalence would be represented by the following thicknesses: 4 mm. of lead, 12 mm. of aluminum, and 5 cm. of water.

This effect becomes evident in Rossi's curves, in which the maximum is characteristically situated for each element; it is also observed in cloud-chamber photographs. The dependence upon atomic number is explained, in the theory of showers, in terms of *Bremsstrahlung* (the radiation emitted when a particle passes close to a nucleus) and pair production. In this theory, Z^2, the square of the atomic number, plays an important role. Screens of the same surface density contain a total number of atoms or of nuclei per unit area approximately proportional to $1/Z$, each one having an efficiency proportional to Z^2; hence the total efficiency is proportional to Z. Therefore, to get screens of different materials with equivalent shower-producing power, one must choose their thicknesses so that their surface densities are proportional to $1/Z$. Here is a relationship quite different from the law of absorption mentioned above. The latter depends simply on the density, while in our case we have to consider the number of nuclei and the magnitude of their electrical charge (or atomic number). Later we shall see the reason for this difference.

COSMIC BLOCK-BUSTERS

Showers are sometimes very dense, consisting of large numbers of rays. Anderson and S. Neddermeyer, for example, obtained pictures of showers comprising as many as three hundred particles (Pl. XI). Similarly, Auger and Ehren-fest in 1935 photographed a shower teeming with more than three hundred rays in a volume of the order of a quart. These dense showers naturally produce a very intense ionization in the gas which they traverse; in fact, a shower of n particles must generate n times as many ions as a single electron. Hence they must resemble closely another phenomenon to which we now turn our attention: the cosmic "block-busters," which produce "bursts."

These explosions are detected as sudden "kicks" or blasts of ionization registered by an electrometer (Pl. II). The phenomenon was discovered by Hoffmann in 1927, while he was studying the residual ionization with one of his electrometers, which were celebrated for their sensitivity. He noticed that among the fluctuations of the ion currents about their mean value, certain changes, always *increases* in ionization, were very sudden and very large. These appeared in the recorded curve as "jumps" or "kicks," during which the electrometer received a veritable burst of ionization. In calculating the number of ions which must have suddenly appeared in the gas of the ionization chamber to produce one of these bursts, Hoffmann found it to be enormous—of the order of millions! Naturally enough, speculation was rife as to the nature of the explosion which gives rise to this effect.

During the past decade, much has been learned about bursts with the aid of high-pressure ionization chambers. If one increases the density of a gas by compression, the intensity of ionization also increases. Thus, if one constructs an ionization chamber of large volume, containing argon under 30 atmospheres of pressure, the number of ions appearing in a single burst runs into tens of millions. Studies of the variation of burst frequency with altitude and with the thick-

ness of screen superposed over the apparatus have led physicists to think that the bursts are caused by electrical particles
in the cosmic rays. If these particles are electrons, their number must be very large. A single one of these particles can produce 10^4 ions along its path in the chamber; it is thus necessary that hundreds, and sometimes thousands, of electrons
traverse the chamber simultaneously in order to produce a
Hoffmann burst.

In the light of the studies on showers, these results should
not astonish us at all. Consider, for example, the shower
of Auger and Ehrenfest mentioned above. If it had been
produced in a chamber, 1 quart in volume, filled with argon
under a pressure of 30 atmospheres, this shower would have
given rise to the production of about 10^7 ions, i.e., to a very
respectable Hoffmann burst.

It is interesting to compute the total energy represented
by such an ionization effect. The creation of a pair of ions in
air consumes an energy of about 30 ev.; this is the work required, on the average, to strip an electron off an atom of
nitrogen or oxygen. Thus a Hoffmann burst which produces
10^8 ion pairs uses up 3×10^9 ev. This is just the order of
magnitude of the energies in the primary cosmic rays. In fact,
in order to reach the earth in equatorial regions, a primary
ray must possess at least 2×10^{10} ev. This is about ten times
the energy required to form 10^8 ions. It suffices, then,
that one-tenth of the energy of a single primary particle
should be transmitted to a sufficient multitude of electrons
in order to produce this burst of ionization. We have just
seen that such transmission of energy is possible thanks to
the phenomenon of shower production.

The ionization bursts have been studied by many investigators, and today we possess detailed knowledge concerning

the conditions of their production, the statistical distribution of their sizes, and the frequency of their appearance. Thus, experiments analogous to those of Rossi, in which lead plates of increasing thickness are successively placed over the ionization chamber detecting the bursts, have shown the effect of such screens. They play much the same role in the generation of bursts that is played in shower formation by metallic plates superposed over counters or cloud chambers. The only difference is that the optimum thickness for burst production is much greater than that observed for showers; it is about 3–4 cm. of lead instead of 1 or 2 cm. This thickness is not constant but varies with the type of burst considered: the larger the number of rays in a burst, the more material is required to produce it, i.e., the more energy is needed.

Special arrangements, selecting bursts of a given size (i.e., showers of exactly n rays, n being varied up to 1,000, for example), have shown clearly that the maximum of the burst production curve as a function of thickness is displaced as n varies. Under very great thicknesses of material, the frequency of bursts, like that of showers, does not fall to zero but decreases regularly and slowly. It follows the intensity of the cosmic radiation which gives rise to these secondary phenomena. As one rises into the atmosphere, their number increases very rapidly. Finally, it has been possible to prove that bursts and showers are of the same character by superimposing the apparatus for selective detection of the two phenomena and ascertaining that they occur together in most cases.

THE ATOMIC NUCLEI EVAPORATE

We have seen that the particles appearing in photographs of showers are electrons. However, about 1 per cent of the observed tracks are due to heavier particles. These can be recognized in certain cloud-chamber pictures by the much greater density of their droplets, which corresponds to a more intense production of ions along their paths. These heavy particles might be, a priori, protons or alpha particles—i.e., the nuclei of the two lightest elements, hydrogen and helium. They are principally protons, as is shown by a simultaneous evaluation of their energy and of the ion density along their paths. The question then arises: Whence do these protons come? The fact that frequently several of them appear at once demonstrates their secondary nature. These are not primary particles which have traversed the atmosphere. Certain cloud-chamber pictures have shown a remarkably high number of protons—three, four, five, and even more (Pl. XII). These tracks, radiating from a common point, give the impression that at that point there has occurred a nuclear explosion, resulting in the violent ejection of debris composed of protons and alpha particles. Contrary to what happens in the case of showers, the particles responsible for these tracks do not move preponderantly in the same direction but scatter in all directions.

The photographic-emulsion technique has made an important contribution here, considering the short time that it has been in use. The principle reason for its importance lies in its continuous sensitivity. In taking Wilson photographs of cosmic rays, one must wait several minutes between expansions until the apparatus is again ready for action, and the sensitivity of the artificial fog lasts only a few hundredths of a second. As a result, the ordinary expansion apparatus is really sensitive only for less than one one-thousandth of the duration of the experiments. In the direct photographic method, on the other hand, the sensitive surface is always ready to register the effects of ionizing particles. Thus, if one leaves it for several months to be affected by the action of cosmic rays, one has a good chance of observing, among the ordinary effects of radioactivity, evidence of certain very rare phenomena which have occurred in the course of this time. It is evidently necessary that the great number of the more common effects should not mask these exceptional effects; that is fortunately the case here, since the former, because of radioactive substances in the vicinity of the emulsion, produce a very feeble ionization[9] (due to electrons), while the latter produce very dense ionization (due to protons or alpha particles; see Pl. XIII).

In this way the explosions of which we have just spoken become easy to detect. As has been shown by M. Blau, H. Wambacher, and T. R. Wilkins, they manifest themselves by the appearance in the developed emulsion of microscopic "stars" consisting of as many as five, ten, or more branches, radiating out in random directions from a well-defined point. These branches are usually the tracks of protons, but sometimes also of alpha particles, as was demonstrated in a statistical investigation by M. Shapiro. It is evident that we are dealing here with the effect of a cosmic ray which has struck a nucleus in its passage through matter, for these stars are more numerous when the plates have been exposed at a high altitude (see Pls. XIII, B, C, D; XXI; and XXII). After several weeks of exposure on a high mountain, they appear in considerable numbers. Thus, on a photographic plate exposed on Mount Evans for eight months, Shapiro found more than one hundred "stars" per square centimeter

---

[9] Occasionally, alpha particles from radioactive impurities in the glass, the gelatin, or the paper in which the plates are wrapped do leave dense tracks; but these are usually distinguishable from cosmic-ray phenomena.

of emulsion, as well as a large number of single tracks due to heavy particles. On the other hand, several hours in the stratosphere suffice to furnish a respectable yield of stars.

Niels Bohr has given a strikingly simple explanation of these effects in terms of the "liquid-drop model" of the atomic nucleus. Before describing Bohr's theory, however, we should understand precisely what the physicist means by the word "model." It refers simply to a familiar phenomenon obeying certain rules, to which one compares a new phenomenon that follows rules analogous in form. We shall illustrate this with an example: Let us examine the atomic model of J. J. Thomson, which represents an atom as a large sphere charged with positive electricity, in the interior of which small negative charges occupy suitable positions, about which they vibrate. The neutrality of the atom, composed partly of electrons and partly of positive particles, the vibrations of these electrons about their mean positions, even the successive groups of electrons situated at different energy-levels—all these find their analogues in Thomson's model. However, it was soon proved that the positive particles in the atom are concentrated in a nucleus—far smaller than the region allowed them in the Thomson model—and that the electrons must be outside this nucleus. It was then necessary to abandon the first model and made the electrons revolve in orbits in order that they might continue to move around the nucleus without falling into it. The older model was replaced by the nuclear planetary model of E. Rutherford and Bohr. Indeed, even the latter model, vastly significant and useful as it was, has since been replaced by successively newer models devised to depict more adequately the real behavior of atoms.

In the present case, the "drop" model proposed by Bohr

for the atomic nucleus is based on the fact that a drop of liquid consists of molecules kept together by cohesive forces which are effective only at a distance which is small compared with their diameter. These molecules are agitated by thermal motions which are more or less violent, depending upon the temperature of the drop. They can escape across the bounding surface—that is to say, evaporate—if their movement becomes sufficiently energetic. Similarly, a nucleus is composed of particles much smaller than itself—protons and neutrons; and the speed of their motions determines a sort of nuclear temperature. In general, these particles do not have sufficient speed to overcome the forces of cohesion—forces which can act only at a very small distance.

Let us test our model with an imaginary experiment: Suppose that we rapidly pass a hot metallic needle through the liquid drop, imparting to it some of the needle's energy. This raises the temperature of the drop, which then partly evaporates; i.e., some of its molecules escape. Passing to the atomic domain, let us shoot through the nucleus a very energetic cosmic-ray particle, which, in passing, shares part of its energy with the constituent protons and neutrons. The temperature of the nucleus rises, and several of the elementary particles are able to escape: the nucleus partly evaporates. The loss of energy to which the drop (or the nucleus) is subject during this evaporation restores its temperature to a value at which cohesion regains the upper hand; and the state of affairs prior to the disturbance is re-established, except that a smaller drop or nucleus remains. Of course, the energy of an escaping molecule in the evaporating drop of water is only a fraction of an electron-volt, while, in order for a proton or neutron to leave the nucleus, many millions of times as much energy is required.

These are the "evaporated" particles which by their dense ionization form the star tracks in photographic emulsions. Each star is produced at a point where a nucleus, heated by the passage of a cosmic particle, is partially vaporized. These nuclear evaporations, moreover, when produced in the gas of an ionization chamber, should give rise to Hoffmann bursts, thanks to the very strong ionizing power of the heavy particles.

These stars are, however, much rarer than showers. Their important role seems to be the production of neutrons. The particles emitted in a nuclear evaporation should consist about equally of protons and of neutrons, these two types being present in comparable numbers in the nuclei. In passing through matter, the protons lose their energy very rapidly by producing intense ionization; therefore they are stopped very soon. Neutrons, on the other hand, travel large distances before they are slowed down by collisions, converted into slow neutrons, and finally absorbed by certain types of nuclei.[10] One can thus predict that in the cosmic rays there should exist a neutron component. These particles have, in fact, been detected recently by diverse methods—in particular, by the artificial radioactivity they excite in nuclei which have absorbed them.

S. A. Korff has constructed neutron counters by filling conventional cosmic-ray counters with boron trifluoride. Slow neutrons entering such a counter have a good chance of interacting with the nuclei of boron atoms, ejecting alpha particles. The latter produce an intense ionization which can be distinguished from that due to an electron by suitably adjusting the counter voltage. With such apparatus it has been

---

[10] Certain nuclei, which are especially subject to reactions with slow neutrons, show exceptionally high absorbing power for these particles.

shown that the number of neutrons increases rapidly as one rises in the atmosphere, following a law similar to that which governs the increase with altitude of nuclear evaporations. It may be that these phenomena are somehow related.

The assortment of cosmic phenomena which we have described will surely be augmented by new types in the future; perhaps the "explosive showers" whose existence, predicted by W. Heisenberg, has not yet been verified experimentally, will be the next conquest in this domain, so full of the unforeseen. We shall in the next chapter introduce the reader to one of the most remarkable newcomers in the cosmic "fauna," which, for all its novelty, has been given the name "mesotron," reminiscent of paleontology.

CHAPTER FOUR

Time Takes Its Toll of Cosmic Rays

IT WILL be recalled that the form of the absorption curves in air and water led to the idea that the cosmic radiation reaching the lower atmosphere is a mixture of at least two components of very different penetrating powers. It is worth noting that the absorption studied hitherto took place within the very medium in which the detecting apparatus was placed. The further to investigate the two-component hypothesis, we shall now interpose in the path of the cosmic rays absorbing screens which are more amenable to experimental control.

THE HARD AND THE SOFT

Let us superpose two counters with their axes parallel and then successively interpose between these counters absorbing materials, such as lead plates, of varying thicknesses. Next let us connect the counters into a coincidence circuit. Then only those particles which traverse the plates and both counters can give rise to a simultaneous discharge of the two detectors, i.e., to a coincidence. The amount of matter present in the counters is so meager that it can deflect or intercept only an insignificant fraction of the passing cosmic rays. Practically all of the absorption occurs in the plate, so that by measuring the number n of coincidences per hour for various thicknesses we can plot an absorption curve for the particles with n as ordinate and the thickness x as abscissa.

The curves obtained (Rossi, Auger) at sea-level with lead plates have a very characteristic shape (Fig. 13, curve I). The number n decreases very rapidly as x increases from 0 to 8 cm.; then the slope of the curve changes to a much smaller

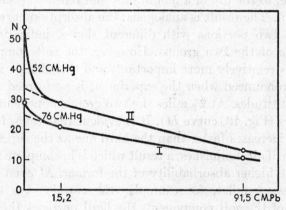

FIG. 13.—Curve showing the absorption by lead of the vertical cosmic rays. Curve I, sea-level. Curve II, altitude of about 2 miles. An abrupt drop over the first 10 cm. of lead is followed by a slower decrease in intensity. This drop (due to absorption of the soft component) is much faster at a high altitude.

value, which it maintains up to a thickness of 3 feet, the limit reached in these experiments. The change in slope occurs when about a third of the rays have been absorbed. These facts led the author to postulate the existence of two groups of particles with quite different properties: one, called the "soft component," is entirely absorbed by 10 cm. of lead; the other, called the "hard component," can penetrate more than ten times this thickness. However, it will be noted that these are the very characteristics of the two groups we have previously cited. Hence, from experiments with such an absorbing screen one can deduce the relative numbers of these two species of particles. It has been found that the ratio of their abundance at sea-level is approximately one soft particle to two penetrating ones.

Let us now raise the apparatus well above sea-level—for example, to the top of a mountain—and repeat the same experiment. The result is analogous: the absorption curve consists of two portions with different slopes, indicating the presence of the two groups. However, the soft component becomes relatively more important, and this change is even more pronounced when the experiment is performed at still higher altitudes. At $2\frac{1}{5}$ miles the two groups appear in equal numbers (Fig. 13, curve *II*). It is evident that the soft component increases faster than the hard one as the superposed stratum of air diminishes, a result which is in complete accord with the higher absorbability of the former. At even higher altitudes—9 miles, for example—the cosmic rays consist largely of the soft component, the hard particles then constituting only 20 per cent of the total radiation. On the other hand, if one descends underground below depths of rock equivalent to about 80 feet of water, the soft component becomes comparatively unimportant.[1]

These are the experimental facts. What can we conclude from them as to the relationship between the two types of radiation? A priori, different hypotheses are possible. Thus, one of the groups might be primary, the other secondary, the latter being born in the atmosphere as the progeny of the former. In this case, it would be natural to think of the pene-

[1] However, this group does not diminish to less than one- or two-tenths of the total radiation, regardless of the thickness of absorber superposed.

trating group as primary and the soft group as terrestrial in origin. On the other hand, one might postulate that the two groups are independent of one another and that each is absorbed according to a law of its own. Finally, these two hypotheses may have to be combined. For example, one or each of the two types of particles may itself be a composite of several groups, not all of which are related to the other type. We shall see that only the last supposition is tenable.

Suppose that the soft component is the progeny of the hard radiation. How can this secondary group increase faster than the primary one with rising altitude? Similarly, the hard radiation cannot be entirely a secondary component of the soft radiation, for it should then decrease as one rises, since its penetrating power is so great that the atmosphere hardly stops it. On the other hand, the two groups cannot be quite independent, for if that were the case, the less penetrating group should be altogether absent at great depths underground, while experience shows that it persists, though in small proportions.[2] These soft rays are certainly the secondaries of hard rays. The relation between the hard and the soft radiations appeared, therefore, to be very complex. It could not be elucidated until we had a more precise idea as to the nature of each of these groups of particles and as to how this nature determines their respective penetrating powers.

We are accustomed to expect the penetrating power of particles to vary rapidly with their energy, and usually the particles with greater energy are the more penetrating. For example, the electrons which constitute the beta rays of radioactive substances can pass through more matter, the

---

[2] Another argument in favor of the close relation between the two groups derives from the fact that the effect of the earth's magnetic field is practically the same on both.

greater their speed. Ordinarily, however, the penetrating power varies in a regular fashion with the speed; and, in order to explain the enormous difference between the soft and hard groups, it seemed necessary to suppose that the respective particles have mean energies which are extremely different. Thus the hard particles would be electrons of high energy, forming a homogeneous group; and the soft particles, electrons of relatively low energy.[3] Turning, then, to the theoreticians, the experimentalists asked them to examine the question of the relationship between the penetrating power and the energy of electrons.

THE THEORETICIANS STICK TO THEIR GUNS

It must be admitted that this question embarrassed the theoreticians not a little. They were able to calculate the penetrating power of electrons up to energies of several hundred millions of electron-volts, but beyond that the quantum hypotheses which they took as the basis of their calculations could be considered only as very adventurous conjectures. However, they went resolutely to work and announced—but not, at first, with very much conviction—a surprising conclusion: the penetrating power of electrons should stop increasing beyond a certain critical energy. The phenomena responsible for this upper limit on penetration are none other than those we encountered in the preceding chapter under the names "pair creation" and "*Bremsstrahlung*."

It is, in fact, easy to see that what limits the penetrating power of a particle is the amount of energy it must relinquish

[3] One should note the importance of the word "relative" here, for when we speak of "low energy" in the case of a cosmic-ray electron, the particle may still possess many times as much energy as the most powerful machines in our laboratories are able to communicate to an electron.

to the medium in which it travels. If a particle, even of feeble energy, pierces a body without imparting to the aggregations of atoms in its path an appreciable portion of its energy, as is the case for electrically neutral particles (neutrons), its penetrating power can be extremely great. If, on the other hand, a highly energetic particle distributes its energy generously among the atoms near which it passes, it will be stopped very soon. It is this last case which confronted the theoreticians in their investigation of fast electrons, thanks to the latter's minute mass and electrical charge. A very fast electron produces photons in passing near nuclei, thus losing a very considerable portion of its energy; these photons constitute the *Bremsung* radiation, which in turn creates pairs. In short, our fast electron gives birth to a shower. We are then at a loss to understand the nature of the hard component whose existence is shown by experience. For no matter what energy we attribute to the electrons which could constitute it,[4] they should never be able, according to the theoreticians, to penetrate more than a few centimeters of lead. They should be stopped after having produced a more or less abundant shower.

In view of the results of this calculation, it became essential to assure, by means of experiments as direct as possible, that there really exist single particles capable of piercing scores of centimeters of lead and producing tracks identical with those of electrons in an expansion chamber. To do this, two cloud chambers were placed by Auger and Ehrenfest above and below a mass of lead about 50 cm. thick. A Geiger-Müller counter was placed above the top chamber and another below the bottom one; these were connected in a coin-

---

[4] Up to extremely high energies, like 10^{15} ev., where the theory must probably be altered.

cidence circuit. A particle had to cross both counters in order to discharge them, and expansions were therefore initiated only when it passed through the first chamber, then the lead, then the second chamber. Many pictures were thus obtained in which one could recognize unmistakably above and below the lead the track of one and the same particle, generally but slightly deviated in its passage through the thick plate (Pl. XIV). Confronted with these photographs, the theoreticians declared that the particles could not, under any circumstances, be electrons. The authors of these experiments then concluded that the penetrating rays might perhaps consist of protons.

Two schools of thought arose among the physicists struggling with these difficulties. The one, showing more confidence in the theoreticians than the latter themselves possessed, decided that the hard component cannot consist of electrons. The other, undoubtedly more prudent, spoke of a domain of energy in which the ordinary quantum theory is no longer applicable and asked the theoreticians to try their calculations again, but to build them on a less fragile foundation.

Plunging again into these laborious mathematics, the theoreticians then analyzed more thoroughly the phenomenon of the retardation of electrons by matter. H. A. Bethe and W. Heitler, then H. J. Bhabha and Heitler, and J. F. Carlson and J. R. Oppenheimer, derived expressions for the energy loss of electrons and the transformation of this energy into showers. This theory could be applied at once to the experiments on shower creation which had been previously carried out and which we described in chapter iii (the Rossi curve and the cloud-chamber experiments). The theory was found to be in reasonable agreement with the results of those experiments.[5] Encouraged by this success, the theoreticians averred that they could do no better and that electrons with energies exceeding several hundred million volts should be unable to survive passage through a lead plate scores of centimeters thick. But the well-established fact is that the hard cosmic rays do penetrate such thicknesses. Accordingly, it became absolutely necessary to measure directly the energy of these particles in order to see how this energy is related to their penetrating power.

THE COSMIC RAYS REVEAL THEIR ENERGY

We have already indicated that if a Wilson chamber is placed in a sufficiently intense magnetic field, the track of an ionizing particle is bent into a circular arc. From the radius of the arc we can find the momentum of the particle. If, in addition, we know its mass, then we can deduce its energy. Numerous experiments have been performed with cloud chambers placed in a strong magnetic field, i.e., between the poles of an electromagnet or in a solenoid. To investigate simultaneously the penetrating power of the particles, a plate, generally consisting of lead, is placed horizontally in the middle of the chamber in the path of the rays.

Under these conditions one can measure the curvature of the track above the plate, as well as that below the plate. Thus it is possible to evaluate not only the energy of a cosmic-ray particle (assumed to be an electron) upon its arrival in the chamber but also the portion of this energy which is lost in crossing the plate (Pl. X). From statistics on the change in curvature, Anderson became convinced of the need for distinguishing between two groups—a need which we

[5] No real quantitative test can be obtained because of our lack of knowledge of the energy spectrum of the soft component (electrons) at sea-level.

have already encountered in the experiments on absorption. The particles in one group were subject to high energy loss in crossing the plate; indeed, some of these were stopped completely. They were, moreover, frequently accompanied by secondary electrons and showers. The particles in the remaining group, however, lost but a small fraction of their energy in traversing the plate and were unaccompanied by secondaries in their passage through the chamber. In these two groups one easily recognizes the character of electrons, on the one hand, and that of the particles in the hard component, on the other, the former giving birth to showers by successive processes of *Bremsstrahlung* and pair formation, the other showing relatively slight interaction with matter.

Other investigators soon confirmed these results. Certain factors, however, complicated the interpretation of these phenomena. One was the fact, demonstrated by Blackett, that the particles of the hard component and those of the soft group usually showed energies of quite distinct magnitudes. It remained difficult to find evidence in these experiments for two particles of the same energy with radically different behaviors. To be sure, the two energy domains did meet at about 2×10^8 ev., but no one had an adequate explanation for the very weak overlapping of the soft and hard components.

We might pause to inquire as to what are the highest energies for which measurements of curvature have been made. For the particles in the hard component, which alone can attain and exceed 10^9 ev., the measurements of Leprince-Ringuet, made on hard particles selected by their passage through 10 cm. of lead, enabled him to reach a value of 2×10^{10} ev. This energy is, moreover, certainly not the upper limit, for in every series of experiments there appears a certain percentage of tracks which are not visibly bent by the magnetic field and which are, consequently, due to particles of still higher energy.

THE THEORETICIANS ARE VINDICATED

There was nothing left for the experimental physicists but to incline toward the results of the theoreticians and to concede that the hard particles were, in fact, not electrons. The theoreticians went further and showed that to explain the penetrating character of the hard component it is enough to attribute to these particles a mass a few scores or a few hundreds of times as great as that of electrons. Thus it became unnecessary to invoke the proton theory.

At this time the Japanese mathematician H. Yukawa devised a working hypothesis which was destined to have great success. He was seeking to elucidate the important question of the origin of intranuclear forces, i.e., the forces which bind the constituent protons and neutrons together within a nucleus. Earlier the Italian physicist E. Fermi had tried to interpret intranuclear forces by assuming that these forces arise from the exchange of electrons between the protons and neutrons. Although it was excellent from a formal point of view, Fermi's theory predicted an order of magnitude for these forces which was inadequate to explain the results of experiments. Yukawa then supposed that the particle exchanged between proton and neutron is not an electron but a heavier particle endowed with very special properties. He called this particle a "heavy quantum," but it is now known as either "mesotron" or "meson" (from the Greek word meaning "intermediate").

From this it was but a single step to suppose that these new particles of Yukawa constitute the hard component of the cosmic rays. Indeed, this identification supplied the key to most of the difficulties which had impeded progress in interpreting the observed effects. Thus, for example, the evaluations of the mass of the cosmic-ray mesotron which have been obtained by different methods have yielded results in agreement with Yukawa's prediction: the mesotron is about two hundred times as massive as the electron. Unfortunately, the methods employed in determining the mass are generally based on measurements of the ionizing power of the particles—measurements which lack precision. Recently Leprince-Ringuet obtained a Wilson picture of a collision between a mesotron and an electron. Since the energies of the particles proved to be quite measurable, thanks to their magnetic curvature, an analysis of the mechanics of the collision enabled him to determine[6] the ratio between the mass of the mesotron and that of the electron; he found a value of 240.

By way of summary, we may say that at sea-level the cosmic radiation is composed essentially of two groups of particles: electrons presenting an energy spectrum with an upper limit of several hundred millions of electron-volts, and mesotrons showing an energy spectrum which begins where that of the electrons stops and which extends much further than our methods of measurement have permitted us to investigate.

A PHANTOM PARTICLE

At the beginning of this chapter we described the difficulties which present themselves when one tries to understand the relationship between the two types of cosmic-ray parti-

---

[6] With an accuracy of about 10 per cent.

cles. Is one of these groups primary with respect to the other; and, if so, which is the progenitor and which the offspring? It has been possible to answer this question, thanks to the ephemeral character of the new particle. Yukawa, not being content with predicting its mass, was also led to endow it with a strange property—an exceedingly short lifetime. The mesotron dies a few millionths of a second after its birth. This peculiarity is related, in a way which we cannot describe here in detail, to beta radioactivity, i.e., the spontaneous transmutation of certain atomic nuclei with the emission of electrons.

Again the word "spontaneous," which we condemned at the beginning of this work, has intruded into our discussion. One might maintain that this spontaneity serves no other purpose here than to mask our provisional ignorance of the real conditions of disintegration. And one might suppose that there exists an internal complexity which, once it were understood, would be found to be governed by ordinary deterministic causality. Let us observe, however, that in the case of the mesotron it is an elementary particle and not a composite nucleus which disintegrates spontaneously. This makes the hypothesis of an internal mechanism very risky. It is actually more logical to prepare ourselves to integrate these spontaneities on the atomic scale into a general system, in which probability would cease to be the mask of ignorance and would represent an extension of the concept of causality.

Before going further, let us answer at once a question which has probably occurred to the reader. How is it possible to observe such particles if they disappear several microseconds after their birth? Here, again, it is ionization which providentially furnishes a means of detection (Pl. XV). Thanks to their great speed, the mesotrons are able, during their brief existence, to traverse great distances; and their path in a gas is delineated by a large number of ions.[7]

It should also be noted that, in consequence of the high speed of mesotrons, any estimate of their life-span must take into account the relativity of time and space. It is only in their own time scale, that of a clock carried along with the same speed, that the mesotrons live several microseconds. In the time scale of the observer who sees them pass by, their lifetime can be considerably longer, thanks to the Lorentz-Fitzgerald contraction of time. Hence the mean lifetime of mesotrons in motion is subject to a correction which can be very important. In the observer's frame of reference the faster mesotrons appear to live longer, and consequently cross greater distances before decomposing.[8]

What becomes of the mesotron's energy (mass energy as well as kinetic energy) when it dies? There is considerable evidence, as we shall see later, that the disintegration gives rise to an electron possessing the same charge. Moreover, this transformation occurs "spontaneously" and does not require the proximity of other matter.

At this point the critical reader may well ask an embarrassing question: How can you reconcile this new transformation, which takes place far from any nucleus, far from any third body such as that which participates in the creation of electron pairs, with the principles to which you cling so tenaciously? It is, indeed, impossible to answer this question

[7] As a matter of fact, in the expansion chamber the track of a fast mesotron is indistinguishable from that of an electron of comparable energy, the number of ions created per centimeter of path being virtually the same.

[8] The distance traveled does not depend upon the speed, except through the effect of the latter upon the time contraction, for the absolute value of this speed is always close to that of light and does not change appreciably when the energy is augmented by several millions of electron-volts.

so long as we content ourselves with observable particles, i.e., with the mesotron before the event and an electron of the same charge afterward.[9] If all the energy of the first particle were transferred to the second, then the principle of conservation of energy would be respected but that of the conservation of momentum would be violated, since the mass of the mesotron is much greater than that of the electron. We can get a clear idea of the nature of this difficulty if we suppose that a mesotron located in a vacuum at the moment of observation has been completely stopped by successive retardations and is stationary with respect to the observer. It possesses no kinetic energy and no momentum but a mass energy of 10^8 ev. If it emits only an electron upon disappearing, then its mass energy must be converted into the electron's kinetic energy. The latter would thereby acquire a considerable impulse in some direction—an impulse which would have been "created" in violation of the principle of conservation of momentum. This is, indeed, a dilemma: we are in a vacuum, far from matter, and in order to adhere to our principles it is necessary at all costs to have a third body. Such a body, flying off in a direction opposite to that of the electron, could conserve the momentum of the system.

The loyalty of physicists to their time-tested principles is not easily shaken. Being unable to find a third body, they were willing to "invent" one. Happily, in the present case the required particle had already been "invented" by W. Pauli in order to satisfy the conservation principles in another phenomenon—the beta radioactivity of atoms. It is known that the nucleus of radium D (radiolead), for example, emits an electron during its transmutation into radium E. In order

---

[9] These charges are equal and of the same sign, in accordance with the principle of conservation of electricity.

that energy and momentum be conserved, it is necessary here, too, that a third body should also be emitted. However, this particle gives no evidence of its existence by any observable effect. In particular, no ionization is produced, either close to the radioactive atom or at some distance from it, that cannot be attributed to the electrons and photons which are normally emitted.

Our particle must therefore be without electric charge; it must be neutral. Moreover, its mass must be very small, compared with that of the neutron. Hence it has been given the name "neutrino," or "small neutron." Finally, it does not interact with the matter it traverses (it cannot be detected by ionization) and is therefore a very penetrating particle. All these qualities are negative: no charge, hardly any mass, negligible interaction with matter. It is a phantom which passes through anything and is affected by nothing.

This, then, is the swan song of a moribund mesotron. It disappears while projecting into space in two opposite directions an electron and a neutrino. All of its charge goes into the electron, while its mass energy is divided between the two particles in kinetic form.[10] The total impulse remains zero if the speeds of the two particles are suitably related to one another, and we have enough confidence in our physical principles to be certain that they are.

EPITAPH TO A MESOTRON

Various interesting corollaries follow from the fact that mesotrons are mortal. In the first place, they must be secondary in character. For how could these ephemeral particles reach the top of our atmosphere from interstellar space if

[10] Approximately 5×10^7 ev. are imparted to the electron.

they do not live long enough to travel more than a few scores of miles? It must therefore be in the stratospheric layers of our own atmosphere, at a height of about 15 miles, that the mesotrons are born. We shall return later to this question of the production of mesotrons in the atmosphere.

Another consequence of the mortality of mesotrons is the abundant production in the lower atmosphere of "decay electrons," each arising from the decomposition of a single mesostron. This origin is, in fact, attributed to a large portion of the electrons in the soft component at sea-level. Confirmation of this hypothesis comes from observations of the variation with geomagnetic latitude of the mesotrons and electrons at sea-level and below, under strata of water or soil. The frequencies of these two types of particles are there maintained in constant ratio; this shows their interdependence. We shall soon see, however, that this explanation is less satisfactory for the electrons in the soft component at very high altitudes, which are much more numerous than the mesotrons at those heights.

A necessary concomitant of the "absorption with time" of mesotrons is their "absorption by space": the longer they travel, the greater is their chance of disappearing. This, in turn, affects the angular distribution of intensities in the hard cosmic rays. Those mesotrons which pass through the atmosphere obliquely traverse longer distances in the rarefied air than those traveling down vertically. Hence the former are more likely to disintegrate in crossing a layer of air of given height than are the vertical mesotrons. Generally speaking, disintegration plays an important role, compared to other types of absorption, when the mesotrons are passing through a material of low density, like the atmosphere. On the other hand, it accounts for only negligible absorption when the mesotrons are traveling in a dense material. In the latter case the energy which the particles lose by ionization stops them well before they have a chance of dying a natural death.

From precise measurements on these effects it has been possible to deduce the mean lifetime of the mesotron, i.e., the interval of time during which it has an even chance of disappearing by decomposition.[11] One can compare, for example, the decrease in the number of mesotrons passing through 0.6 mile of atmosphere with the diminution in the same number traversing 10 cm. of lead. The absorption by each of the two materials, if due only to ionization, ought to be the same; and, if more mesotrons disappear in the 0.6 mile of air, it is due to the longer time (*relatively:* we are dealing here with several millionths of a second!) of this traversal. During this time, disintegrations occur which do not have time to take place in the 10-cm. path in the lead. The lifetime, thus measured, has been found to be of the order of 2 or 3 microseconds.

Recently new methods have been devised by F. Rasetti, by Auger and R. Maze, and by Rossi and N. Nereson, in order to measure this lifetime. These methods are more direct than the preceding ones, for they consist in recording the passage of a mesotron through some counters, followed by the detection of its disintegration electron as the latter passes through other counters. The time which separates the two events measures the lifetime of the particular mesotron observed, and statistics covering a large number of cases yield a value of the mean lifetime.

It must be understood, however, that measurements of

[11] It should be observed that mesotrons, like radioactive atoms, do not age, even though they are mortal. They have at every instant of their life the same chance of surviving during the next microsecond as during the preceding one.

this kind are possible only on mesotrons which have been stopped by passage through dense blocks of matter. A mesotron traveling at full speed does not spend enough time near the counters to have a very good chance of expiring in the vicinity of our apparatus and leaving evidence of its decomposition in the registration of its electron progeny. One of the experimental difficulties arises from the very fact that only a small fraction of the mesotrons detected by the first counter set are stopped in the blocks of iron or aluminum interposed in their path. Registrations of both mesotron and electron are therefore very rare, but patience is not a rare virtue among physicists. They have accumulated the necessary data and have found the mean lifetime measured by these methods to be approximately 2 microseconds.[12] This value is in qualitative agreement with those deduced from indirect measurements. However, the discrepancy between the results of the two methods exceeds the estimated experimental error. Its interpretation will perhaps be found in the recently discovered production of mesotrons in the low atmosphere.

Indubitably, this collection of experiments on the hard component provides a substantial body of evidence for the model of the mesotron which we have described: a particle whose rest mass is more than two hundred times the electronic mass, carrying an elementary electric charge, positive or negative, and decomposing spontaneously after a mean lifetime of 2 microseconds into an electron of the same charge and a neutrino. However, in order to be completely satisfied, the physicists wanted to "see" this decomposition. They desired to utilize their sixth sense, that of ionization, in order to assure the reality of this phenomenon. E. J. Williams, then

---

[12] Very recently Rossi and Nereson have published a more precise value of the lifetime.

T. Johnson, S. de Benedetti, and R. P. Shutt, took a large number of pictures of low-energy mesotron tracks with an expansion chamber containing a gas under pressure, in order to increase the chances of stopping a mesotron right inside the chamber. They had to take several tens of thousands of photographs in order to find a few showing the dense (i.e., heavily ionized) track of a mesotron ending in the gas of the chamber. On two of these, a very fine track, that of an electron, originated at the very spot where the mesotron was stopped dead. Anderson and Neddermeyer placed a counter in the middle of a cloud chamber filled with argon and obtained a picture of a mesotron coming to rest in the gas of the chamber (Pl. XVI). More recently, W. Bostick obtained a photograph showing a heavy particle incident upon a lead plate and a fast electron emerging below (Pl. XVII). The neutrino, because of its phantom nature, eludes all our senses, including the sixth.

CHAPTER FIVE

The Sky's the Limit

HAVING acquired some definite notions about the nature of the particles in the cosmic rays, we are in a position to get a clearer picture of these rays—a picture based on a more exact knowledge of their energies. In an earlier chapter we described the variation with latitude of the intensity of the radiation reaching the earth. From this variation we can deduce the distribution of the particles as a function of their energy, i.e., the "energy spectrum" of the primary rays upon their arrival in the atmosphere. We have learned in this way that there exists a minimum energy of about 1.2×10^9 ev. for primary particles.

On the other hand, this geomagnetic method is limited in its application to values less than 6×10^{10} ev.,[1] whereas there is evidence that certain particles possess energies exceeding this value by as much as a power of 10. Unfortunately, the technique of utilizing an expansion chamber placed in a magnetic field does not enable us to exceed the same limit either. In fact, it is at just about 2×10^{10} ev. that the magnetic curvature of the track of a charged particle ceases to be measurable in the apparatus which we actually possess.

---

[1] Particles possessing an elementary charge and an energy above 6×10^{10} ev. may be considered insensitive to the earth's magnetic field.

There are two methods, however, which permit a considerable shift of this limiting value and greatly extend our knowledge of the energy spectrum of the total cosmic radiation. One of these is applicable only to the hard cosmic rays, and we shall examine this method first.

CALCULATIONS IN BILLIONS

We have already noted that the particles of the hard group—the mesotrons—lose their energy by ordinary ionization. This means that the only process which consumes the energy of such a particle is the production of ions along its path. It follows that the loss of energy along the track is practically linear in a material of constant density; in other words, the loss per unit path is proportional to the density of the medium. Moreover, it has been proved that within very wide limits the ionization loss of charged particles does not depend upon their energy when the latter exceeds a certain value, which is of the order of millions of electron-volts for mesotrons. Thus a mesotron of very great energy which, for example, penetrates into the ground or into a body of water loses its energy progressively and in proportion to its descent at a rate of approximately 2×10^8 ev. per yard of water, or per thickness of absorber of equivalent mass.

Once the particle has been retarded sufficiently for its energy to drop below the critical value previously mentioned, the remaining energy is used up more rapidly, since slow particles produce a denser ionization. This, however, is only a terminal phenomenon. Throughout the really important part of the track, it is the regular type of loss described above that occurs. Knowing this, we have a criterion which permits us to evaluate mesotron energies much greater than those measurable by the method of magnetic curvature. Since there is very little creation of mesotrons at sea-level, all the hard particles arriving at the surface of the earth penetrate the ground or water and lose their energy in proportion to the distance traversed. Those particles which can still be detected at a given depth must have been able to penetrate the overlying rock—of thickness equivalent to, say, h yards of water—and therefore must have possessed a certain minimum of energy upon arrival at the earth. The value of this lower limit in electron-volts is obtained by multiplying the number h by 1.5×10^8. Measurements of the relative numbers of particles still present at different depths under water or under ground have been made, and the general result may be summed up as follows: The number of particles per unit time which reach a depth of h yards of water-equivalent is inversely proportional to the square of h.

Utilizing the fact that the loss of energy is proportional to the density of the material traversed, this result can be translated into a spectral distribution of energies in the mesotron radiation arriving at sea-level. This distribution is such that the number n of particles with energies exceeding E is inversely proportional to the square of E. Actually, this law is not quite rigorous; and, instead of $n = E^{-2}$, we should write $n = E^{-\gamma}$, where $\gamma = 1.8$ approximately.[2] What is remarkable about the form of this distribution law is that it does not indicate an upper limit to the energy of the particles. In fact, the presence of mesotrons has been detected at all the depths at which measurements have been attempted, i.e., down to about 1 mile of water-equivalent. The energy possessed at sea-level by mesotrons capable of reaching such depths must exceed 3×10^{11} ev. Thus we have here already increased the upper limit of energy by a factor of nearly 10

[2] This exponent is subject to still further correction.

over that attainable by magnetic measurements. It should be observed that, although there seems to be no upper limit to the energies of individual particles, the total energy—obtained by integrating the spectral distribution curve over values of E up to infinity—tends toward a finite limit. This is, of course, what we should expect physically, and the value of the exponent is such as to yield this result. Thus calculated the total energy of the cosmic rays reaching the earth is of the same order of magnitude as the energy which comes to us from all the stars (except the sun) in the form of light.

Investigations of the soft component of the cosmic radiation also yield some extremely high energy values, but by a quite different method. It will be recalled that, while mesotrons lose energy only by ionization, electrons lose energy chiefly by *Bremsstrahlung* and the creation of showers. We may turn once more to the theoreticians, since their calculations have agreed so well with the experimental results, and ask them what happens when electrons of higher and higher energy pass through matter. Let us select a specific case, that of an electron of 10^{12} ev., i.e., a million million electron-volts. We learn with surprise that, after this particle has crossed the atmosphere, it is no longer capable of producing a single secondary electron. Upon entering the atmosphere it does, to be sure, produce a shower, which grows very abundant after penetrating a thickness of air equivalent to several yards of water. This shower, however, is completely absorbed in the middle atmosphere, so that none of its electrons or photons can reach sea-level. It is only for incident electrons of still higher energy, of the order of 10^{13} ev., that a few electronic descendents—great-great-grandchildren of the initial particle—can arrive as a sole remnant at the bottom of the atmosphere. This explains why, as have we previously mentioned, the soft component detectable in the very low atmosphere is composed almost exclusively of disintegration electrons from mesotrons. At sea-level the electrons formed by shower processses from primary particles constitute scarcely one-thirtieth of the total radiation. It is only at altitudes of several miles that the electrons and photons of direct electronic descent become of principal importance in the soft component.

A HAIL OF ELECTRONS

The question now arises as to how we can find evidence for the exceptional showers which in extreme cases descend as far as sea-level. In other words, how can we separate out of the mixture of rays in the soft component at sea-level that portion which is of purely electronic descent, as opposed to that which arises from the decomposition electrons originating in mesotrons? Once more it is necessary to turn to the methods based on the detection of coincidences between counters.

Let us examine the causes of these coincidences in detectors placed in the open air. Consider first a high-energy electron which is created in the lower atmosphere by the disintegration of a mesotron. It will give rise to a shower which is more or less abundant, depending on its energy, but which, because it originates so close to earth, cannot acquire a very large angular spread. These "small atmospheric showers" can be detected by means of counters placed several centimeters or several decimeters from one another without any dense material above them. A coincident discharge of the counters must be due to the simultaneous arrival of a group of electrons spread over several centimeters or several decimeters. Such a coincidence happens about once per minute when three counters with a surface area of several scores of square centimeters are used. The frequency of this phenomenon reveals the important role of the disintegration electrons in the lower atmosphere.

As the distance between the two extreme counters is increased until the observed counting rate drops below a few coincidences per hour, the experimental difficulties multiply. For this reason, there had been no attempt, before 1938, to separate the counters by more than 40 cm. Then, in the hope of detecting more extensive showers, Auger and Maze placed their detectors several yards apart. The number of coincidences observed decreased very sharply with increasing separation of the counters but finally leveled off at about five or six per hour. (This number represents only *significant* coincidences, the fortuitous ones having been subtracted from the observed total.) The fact that this number did not fall to zero showed that, besides the small local showers, there also occur in the atmosphere groups of simultaneous electrons whose tracks are several yards apart. It was necessary to conclude that a new kind of shower is produced in the atmosphere and that it may well be the exceptional shower of purely electronic descent of which we have just spoken.

Upon separating the counters even further, it was found that coincidences could still be observed at separations of 10, and even of 20, yards. This dispelled any remaining doubt that showers covering large areas occur in the atmosphere. Moreover, since high-energy electron pairs have a small angular spread, it was deduced from these observations that the extensive showers in question must be formed at a high altitude.

We may ask: What is the mode of origin of these large atmospheric showers? Do they originate from a mesotron at the moment of its disintegration, like the small showers (of which they would then be a simple extension), or are they due to a primary group? In an attempt to answer these questions, Auger and Maze set out to measure their variation with altitude. Yielding once again to the lure of the mountain peaks, they ascended to a height of $1\frac{3}{4}$ miles and set up their counters at the Observatory of the Pic du Midi in the French Pyrenees. Here they were able to detect coincidences between counters 245 feet apart.

Then, climbing to the Jungfrau Laboratory in the Swiss Alps, situated at an altitude of $2\frac{1}{6}$ miles, they arranged their apparatus on the immense Swiss glaciers and separated their counters progressively up to a distance of a fifth of a mile. One of the counters was located, with the coincidence circuit, in one of the laboratory's observation cabins; the other was placed inside a box on the ice of a near-by mountain pass (Pl. I, A). A cable buried in the snow carried the necessary electrical power from the laboratory; another line, supported in the air by a row of poles, fed the counter pulses into the coincidence circuit. At the greatest distance tried, about 330 yards, they were still able to observe more than one significant coincidence per hour (Fig. 14). In other words, on an average of once per hour there was produced a virtual hail of simultaneous electrons covering an area of at least 25 acres. Auger and Maze did not push this investigation further, since the experimental difficulties increase rapidly with the distance between the counters; thus, in particular, the maximum time which can be allowed for the impulse from the distant counter to reach the laboratory (one-millionth of a second) is just the time required for the signal to travel 330 yards.

In comparing the measurements made in Paris at a separation of 22 yards between the counters with the results obtained at an altitude of $2\frac{1}{6}$ miles for the same distance, they were able to establish an increase by a factor of 10 between the two altitudes, an increase rather larger than that of the soft component. Moreover, the considerable spread of these "extensive showers," as they came to be called, led to the

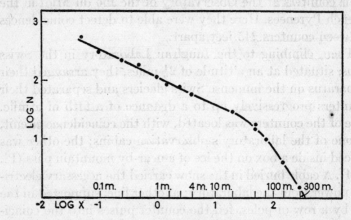

Fig. 14.—Curve showing the decrease in the frequency, N (average number per hour), of extensive showers as a function of the horizontal distance, X, between the counters. The logarithms of N and X are plotted as ordinates and abscissas, respectively. It can be seen that, even when the counters are separated from one another by a distance of 1,000 feet, coincidences are still detected. These must be due to showers which cover an area of the order of 110,000 square feet of the earth's surface. These measurements were made at an altitude of about 2 miles, in the mountain pass of the Jungfrau.

view that they traverse the entire atmosphere, and hence that they originate in a single initial particle—one of those primaries which constitute the cosmic radiation during its passage through interstellar space. These investigations further showed that the number of electrons which reach the ground during the production of a single shower is very large. The density of electrons in this kind of "hail" being of the order of 25 per square yard, one sees that, distributed over an area of 25 acres, more than a million particles arrive simultaneously at the ground.

Finally, it was possible to take pictures of these large showers by controlling an expansion chamber with two counters which could be placed anywhere in the vicinity of the chamber, provided that they were separated from one another by a distance of several yards. The photographs thus obtained showed a type of shower resembling rain, which had already been observed by chance in counter-controlled cloud chambers. It consists of numerous tracks, nearly parallel, indicating that the center of divergence is situated in the air high above the apparatus. These rays also produced more or less abundant showers in the walls of the chamber (Pl. XVIII).

What conclusions can be drawn from these observations about the energy of the primary electrons in the cosmic radiation? Just a while ago, in speaking of the theoreticians' calculations, we showed that only an electron with energy exceeding 10^{12} ev. can produce any noticeable effect after passing through the atmosphere. Here, however, we are concerned not only with the possibility of traversal but also with the production of a million particles which still possess sufficient speed to penetrate our apparatus. What should be the energy of the initial corpuscle? Two methods of evaluation can be tried:

1. According to theoretical calculations, for a particle to produce a million electrons after traveling through the atmosphere, it should possess initially an energy between 10^{15} and 10^{16} ev. [3]

[3] An electron with an initial energy of 10^{15} ev. produces a million particles where the shower is at its maximum. But this happens at an altitude of some 10,000 feet, and at sea-level the number of particles in the showers has already decreased.

2. If we add the total energy of the particles reaching the ground at the instant of arrival of the "hail," using the fact that the mean energy of an electron in the soft component has a value between 10^7 and 10^8 ev., we find a total of approximately 10^{14} ev. This number must then be multiplied by approximately 10, to take into account the various energy losses to which the shower is subjected in its passage through the atmosphere. Part of these losses is due to the ionization produced in the atmosphere by such a shower—an ionization which is truly enormous, as shown by the following calculation. A fast electron creates around 60 ion pairs per centimeter in normal air. Hence a million such electrons traversing three-fifths of a mile of air produce six million millions of these pairs. Since the ionization of a single molecule of air requires 30 ev., the whole shower loses some two hundred million millions of electron-volts per kilometer of normal air traversed!

The two methods, then, indicate a value of the order of 10^{15} ev. for the energy of the generating primary. It may be considered certain, however, that this is not an upper limit, for in these showers which are so full of ordinary cosmic-ray electrons, one can find some evidence, even at sea-level, for the existence of electrons or groups of electrons with energies well above 10^8 ev.; these groups are still capable of producing effects after passing through lead plates 10 cm. thick. In order to account for the presence of some particles possessing such energy among the hail of slower electrons in an extensive shower, we must increase the exponent 15—enormous as it already seems—by one or two units.[4]

[4] It is interesting to compare the energies of such cosmic-ray particles with those involved in ordinary phenomena; one sees, then, that these "very high energies," which require numbers like 10^{15} ev. to describe them, do not, for a single electron,

It should be observed, moreover, that it is only thanks to the formation of these immense showers that we have any knowledge of the existence of corpuscles possessing such high energy. If these particles remained solitary, producing no secondaries, then we could not in any way distinguish them from ordinary mesotrons of several thousand million electron-volts, for their tracks in a Wilson chamber would be absolutely identical, even in the presence of an intense magnetic field. Only the extraordinary fecundity of the high-energy electrons distinguishes them from other particles.

THE WORLD'S HIGHEST LABORATORIES

After all these observations at sea-level or at altitudes of a few miles, physicists were naturally eager to go aloft to investigate events occurring much higher—at altitudes around 19 miles—events which must be responsible for the composition of the cosmic rays observed near the ground. In particular, the production of mesotrons, which rarely occurs at sea-level, should take place in large numbers in the high atmosphere, where the initial particles have not yet crossed the equivalent of 3 feet of water.

Since it was not feasible to carry out experiments at mountain heights greater than 4 miles (in the Caucasus or the Andes), it became necessary to use airplanes or balloons. As for the former, the practicable duration of flight at high altitudes is quite short, and their ceiling does not exceed 6 miles. Hence physicists have resorted to balloons to carry their ap-

---

amount to more than just enough energy to raise the temperature of 1 cubic millimeter of water by 1° C. This comparison shows very well that the striking feature of the cosmic-ray particles is the difference of potential required to accelerate them to their high speeds, i.e., the large number of electron-volts they carry, rather than the absolute value of their kinetic energies.

paratus into the stratosphere, where the cosmic rays reach their maximum abundance.

Everyone remembers the remarkable ascensions of Professor Piccard, of his co-worker M. Cosyns, and of their numerous emulators. These manned balloon flights rose to heights above $15\frac{1}{2}$ miles, which is more than enough for cosmic-ray purposes. However, the very great difficulties of these ascensions, their high cost, and the extremely painstaking preparations necessary to reduce somewhat the great dangers involved have prevented them from becoming a regular method of investigation. A Russian crew met death on one of these expeditions; an American crew had to resort to parachutes to save themselves; and Piccard himself has come through safely only because of his presence of mind and sportsmanship. It is the method of unmanned or free balloons, i.e., small balloons carrying automatic apparatus and not requiring the presence of an operator, which has given us most of the information that we have in this domain. Let us see in some detail how these experiments are carried out.

First, one must construct the instruments for measuring the cosmic radiation—the ionization chambers or sets of counters—so that they will be as light as possible. In fact, the entire equipment, including the detectors, the recording devices, and the batteries which provide power, must not exceed about 45 pounds in weight. By sheer ingenuity physicists have constructed veritable miniature laboratories provided with all the necessary apparatus under fully automatic control. In certain cases, in order to avoid the risk of depending upon records which may be lost with the balloons, the small gondola is equipped with a radio transmitter capable of sending signals continually during the ascension. It goes without saying that in the course of these unmanned flights the atmospheric pressure and the temperature are continually registered or transmitted, since these data are essential for the interpretation of the measurements.

All the equipment is inclosed in a small box consisting of cellophane walls stretched over a framework of light wood. (Light alloys, like Dowmetal, are also frequently used.) Up in the cloudless stratosphere, where the sun shines uninterruptedly, this cellophane inclosure will serve as a sort of "hot box," keeping the apparatus warm enough to operate while the air outside maintains a subarctic temperature. The gondola, comprising the box and its contents, is suspended from a cluster of rubber or latex balloons, filled with hydrogen. These balloons, which are initially inflated to a diameter of about 5 feet, have a great margin for distention, so that, as they encounter lower and lower atmospheric pressure with rising altitude, they can expand progressively to a diameter of 20 feet without bursting. It is often necessary to use twenty-five or more balloons to raise a single set of apparatus.

A day which is not too windy is selected for the ascent; and, after suitable precautions to prevent collision with tall buildings, trees, or telegraph wires, the traditional "Let her go!" signals the release of the apparatus (Pl. XIX). Soon the cluster of balloons and its small gondola shrink into the distance and can no longer be seen except with a telescope. After they have disappeared from view, they continue for a long while to ascend. Then, often after spending a considerable number of hours near their "ceiling," several of the balloons burst, and the others serve as a parachute which brings the apparatus more or less slowly back to earth.

When the measurements are transmitted by radio, the experiment is over as soon as the apparatus falls back to earth; and the work of interpreting the results can be started at once. If, however, the records were registered automatically inside the gondola, then it is essential to recover the apparatus in order to have any results at all. In the latter case the experimenters rely hopefully on the chance that the landing will take place on an inhabited spot and that someone will soon discover the equipment. A card containing the "sender's" address is attached, promising a reward to the finder; while the monetary reward may be small, the idea of collaborating in a scientific experiment generally evokes real enthusiasm. Thus, nine times out of ten, at least, the apparatus is returned after a short delay to its starting-point— in rare instances on the very same day.

Many curious incidents, often quite amusing, attend the departure and arrival of the balloons. Usually the flight extends over a long distance, demonstrating the existence of violent winds in the stratosphere. For example, the apparatus has been discovered 300 miles away after a journey of three hours. One of the more fantastic episodes was the return of a balloon cluster to its starting place after a trip of several hundred miles. This equipment, launched at the University of Chicago, returned ten hours later and landed majestically on the neighboring tracks of the Pennsylvania Railroad, thus ending a stratospheric round trip of considerable extent.

An alarm clock is generally included in the apparatus to record the time and to drive a drum which carries the photographic film. After one flight, a certain farmer, approaching the gondola which had fallen near his barn and hearing a tick-tock sound emanating from the box, was stricken with panic, thinking it must be a delayed-action bomb. Not infrequently, the clusters of balloons are taken for parachute troops during their descent.

Among the difficult take-offs was one that occurred on a

midwinter day in Chicago, with the temperature below zero Fahrenheit, on a football field transformed by the weather into an ice-skating rink. The assistants, thirty in number, who held the balloons, were knocked to the ground by gusts of wind. However, the apparatus sailed up beautifully into the sky once it was launched. Among the less fortunate descents was one that ended in Lake Michigan. The apparatus was fished out after having spent several hours in the water. It must have been endowed with real good will and a lively desire to serve science, to permit recovery even under these conditions and, once found, to relate the story of its adventures.

Let us now examine the information that can be deduced from the results obtained in these flights. In so far as these measurements relate simply to the total ionization or the number of particles which make up the cosmic radiation at various altitudes, they reveal a very rapid increase of these quantities with altitude, followed by a decrease, after a more or less flat maximum (Fig. 4). This maximum occurs when the atmospheric pressure has fallen to about one-twentieth of its value at sea-level. The establishment of this fact is very important, for it shows that the particles keep increasing in number during the first part of their atmospheric path—a multiplication which is evidently due to the formation of showers. The presence of a maximum at a depth of about 20 inches of water-equivalent agrees well with a mean value of the order of 6×10^9 ev. for the energy of the incident particles. Below this maximum region, where the showers are densest, a decrease sets in, absorption becoming more important than multiplication.

It is possible to learn even more from these results by utilizing the action of the earth's magnetic field. At a given location, as we have seen previously, this field deflects away from the earth all electrons which possess less than a certain minimum energy, the exact value of which depends on the latitude. Consequently, if flights are made at two different latitudes and we subtract the effects observed at the lower latitude from those at the higher one, we obtain the effects produced in the atmosphere by the particles contained in a well-defined band of energies. Thus we have seen that at the equator only those electrical particles with energy greater than 1.7×10^{10} ev. can reach the top of the atmosphere. At a latitude of 45°, on the other hand, all those possessing at least 5×10^9 ev. can arrive. The difference between the effects at the equator and those at 45° are due entirely to a group of particles in the energy band between 1.7×10^{10} and 5×10^9 ev. This analysis can be pushed further, and it was by doing so that Millikan and his collaborators were able to give a precise picture of the relative magnitudes of the various energy bands, showing well-defined groups of 2.5×10^8, 5×10^8, 6.6×10^8, and 1×10^9 ev. (Fig. 15).

On the other hand, if we have a precise knowledge of the energies of the incident particles, it is possible to evaluate the effects which they should produce at different points of their penetration through the atmosphere. This calculation can be carried out on the assumption that only shower processes contribute to these effects, and a curve can be drawn showing the ionization to be expected at various depths in the atmosphere. If, on the same diagram, we plot the experimental points obtained from the differences in the ionization at various pairs of latitudes, we can determine to what extent our assumption is valid. The fact is that, at first, in the very

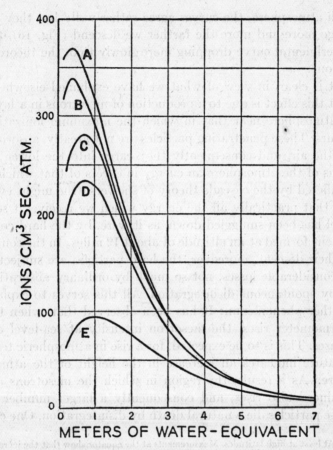

Fig. 15.—Analysis of the effects of groups of cosmic rays of homogeneous energy. These curves show the variation of the intensity of ionization with altitude (expressed in meters of water) at five different latitudes: A, 58° N.; B, 51° N.; C, 45° N.; D, 38° N.; and E, 3° N.

high atmosphere, the curves agree rather well;[5] but they diverge more and more the farther we descend (Fig. 16), the experimental curve dropping more slowly than the theoretical one.

It is clear, in view of what we have explained elsewhere, that this effect is due to a production of mesotrons in a layer of atmosphere near that in which the maximum ionization occurs. These penetrating particles are not greatly absorbed by the air, and consequently they carry into the lower regions of the atmosphere an energy in excess of that which is predicted by the cascade theory of showers. One might even say that practically all the energy which we receive at sea-level has been smuggled down, as it were, by the hard component formed at an altitude of about 12 miles. In the course of their descent, moreover, the hard particles are subjected to considerable losses, not so much by ordinary absorption as by spontaneous disintegration. All this serves to explain another phenomenon: It has been observed that, when the thermometer rises, the mesotron intensity at sea-level decreases. This is to be expected, for a rise in atmospheric temperature indicates an increase in the height of the atmosphere.[6] As a result, the region in which the mesotrons are produced also rises, and consequently a larger number of these particles die a natural death by disintegration. One can

---

[5] At least at high latitudes. Measurements at the equator show that the increase in ionization between the highest altitudes and the maximum is very much smaller than expected. This result is difficult to explain by the cascade theory alone, and it lends some support to the view that most of the primary particles are not electrons.

[6] A similar phenomenon is the "barometric effect," i.e., the decrease in intensity of the cosmic rays when the atmospheric pressure rises. This effect is due partly to increased absorption by the thicker atmosphere and partly to the increased height of the strata where the mesotrons are born.

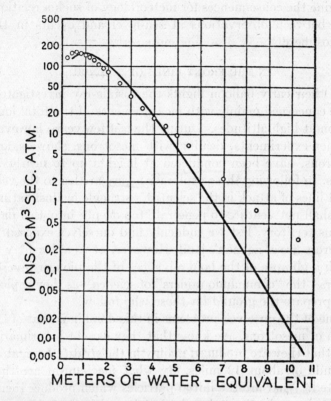

Fig. 16.—The points represent the effects of particles that have an energy of approximately a thousand million electron-volts, according to Millikan, whereas the full curve gives the results predicted by the shower theory of Carlson and Oppenheimer.

imagine the consequences for meteorology of such a relationship between observations at sea-level and events in the stratosphere.

IN THE FRONT LINES OF SCIENCE

In their early balloon flights the cosmic-ray investigators were concerned mainly with measurements of the total ionization at high altitudes. During the last few years, however, further experiments, dealing with mesotrons, showers, and neutrons, have been conducted at heights up to nearly 20 miles. In following these explorations, we are led to the very front lines of attack in the scientist's struggle against nature. We shall not venture to penetrate too deeply into this dangerous territory, lest we suddenly find ourselves exposed to the cross-fire of no man's land. However, let us at least try to catch a glimpse of the bold advances of the pioneer investigators—the "commando raiders" of science—as they explore and prepare the ground for those who follow.

One of the unsolved problems in this domain is that of the birth of mesotrons. We know that they cannot be primaries and that they are produced mainly in the stratosphere, at an altitude of about 12 miles. By what mechanism are they created? What are the initial particles which produce them? Can this production take place at low altitudes? How are the mesotrons related to the extensive showers which originate in the same strata of the atmosphere? These are among the questions to which recent research permits a partial—and only provisional—answer.

To determine whether the mesotrons have their origin in initial penetrating particles or in electrons, "counter telescopes," equipped with lead absorbers from 4 to 18 cm. thick, were sent up in stratospheric balloon flights by M.

Schein, W. P. Jesse, and E. O. Wollan. With this apparatus, which registered only penetrating charged particles, they demonstrated that the mesotrons are produced at very high altitudes, where the atmospheric pressure is no greater than a few decimeters of water-equivalent,[7] and that the cosmic radiation in these regions contains a large number of penetrating rays.

A study of multiple rays in the stratosphere was then carried out by means of a system of coincidence counters capable of recording groups of simultaneous rays produced in a lead plate several centimeters thick. This investigation led Schein and his collaborators to a very surprising result: small groups of mesotrons, about ten at a time, were produced in the lead, while electron showers (containing many particles with low penetrating power), which were expected, appeared only in small numbers. The latter fact agrees, however, with the small percentage of soft radiation found previously at the same altitudes.

It is easy to see how these findings conflict with the hypothesis that mesotrons are produced by initial electrons or photons: the latter would produce mainly showers of soft particles. Furthermore, mesotrons would be present only in small numbers, and probably in pairs, for pair creation is the mechanism which we should expect from the cascade theory even for mesotrons.

On the other hand, the hypothesis of primary protons seems to lend itself more readily to a reasonable explanation. It has been supposed tentatively by Schein and by others that these

[7] The first few decimeters of water-equivalent in the atmosphere extend over an altitude range of many miles, and one cannot speak of a distinct upper limit, or "ceiling," of the atmosphere. So great is the rarefaction of the air at high altitudes that, in order to register the smallest measurable change in pressure, the apparatus must traverse a large vertical distance.

protons of high energy (upward from 10^9 ev.) have a very strong interaction with atomic nuclei and that they produce small mesotron showers containing an average of eight particles when they experience head-on collisions with oxygen and nitrogen nuclei. These mesotrons would constitute the hard component, a certain portion of which reaches the lower levels of the atmosphere.

Of course, it is necessary, on this hypothesis, to account for the electrons which constitute the soft group so abundant in the middle atmosphere. To explain how these come into being, we have at our disposal two modes of production, beginning with mesotrons: knock-on electrons and decay electrons. Knock-on electrons are those which originally move in an orbit of an oxygen or nitrogen atom of the air and with which the mesotron collides violently as it passes by. If the collision is sufficiently direct, the projected electrons ionize and produce showers. As for the decay electrons, we have already seen how they originate. It is noteworthy, however, that when they result from the death of a mesotron in full flight, they acquire its kinetic energy and can then attain much greater energies than the 4×10^7 ev. bequeathed to its offspring by a decaying mesotron which has come to rest. Thanks to these two sources, we can easily populate the atmosphere with the electrons required by the observations.

One nebulous spot remains, however: the relationship between the mesotrons and the extensive showers. We know that the latter require, as a direct cause, an electron or photon of enormous energy, which must be present at the altitudes where the showers are produced. Now, from recent experiments performed on mountain tops and during balloon flights, it seems that the regions at which the extensive atmospheric showers originate extend to very great heights.

For instance, in one balloon flight a set of six counters, arranged along a horizontal bar 33 feet long, was sent up by Auger and A. Rogozinski. Coincidences between the extreme counters, accompanied by many simultaneous discharges of the others, were observed up to about 6 miles, the maximum height attained in this experiment, thus showing that the origin of some of the extensive atmospheric showers occurs still higher.

A BIRD'S-EYE VIEW

It is time to take stock of our accumulated results with a view to synthesizing them into a unified pattern. We shall attempt a systematic survey, starting with the cosmic rays upon their arrival in the outer atmosphere and following their diverse adventures until they disappear by absorption.[8]

In order to make our discussion clear, we shall base it on hypotheses which are currently in vogue. This is a risky procedure, to be sure. But is it not also a game, at once fascinating and fruitful, to explore as far as possible the consequences of these hypotheses, pretending that we believe them even while we remain aware of their weaknesses?

Leaving aside, for a time, that provocative Question No. 1, the question of origin, let us consider a stream of cosmic rays arriving from interstellar space and entering the solar system. What are the properties of these rays? In order to obtain any firsthand information about them, we would have to instal our apparatus in an interplanetary rocket—a startling idea, perhaps, but one which may receive serious consideration in the postwar renaissance of science, when destruction ceases to absorb the minds and energies of men. It would be even

---

[8] Apropos of this, it may be asked: What becomes of all the energy which the cosmic rays carry? It is finally transformed into heat, for this is the form into which all energy is ultimately dissipated.

more convenient to be able to set up a laboratory on the surface of the moon; there no atmosphere would complicate our task by transforming the incoming radiation. Furthermore, the magnetic field of so small a celestial body would probably exert only a very weak influence. Earth-bound as we are, however, we must still send our instruments into the remote stratosphere; and since we rely on balloons to transport them there, it is just as well that there is enough air even at those altitudes to provide the necessary buoyancy. As a result of atmospheric screening, then, we do not know what the composition of the cosmic rays is before their arrival in the atmosphere. We can be certain, however, that the primary radiation does not include any particles whose lifetime is limited by a process of disintegration. Consequently, it contains no mesotrons, and probably no neutrons either. Only electrons and photons—with protons as an additional or alternative possibility—may be constituents of this radiation which fills space isotropically.

Upon their approach toward the earth, the cosmic rays are subject to the influence of the solar, as well as the terrestrial, magnetic fields. As a result, charged particles with insufficient energy are deflected; and the radiation which arrives at the top of the atmosphere consists of two distinct portions: (1) uncharged rays (photons), on the one hand, and protons and electrons of very high energy, on the other, which are affected only slightly or not at all by the magnetic fields; and (2) electrons and protons of lower energy, which are more or less strongly influenced by these fields.

The relative importance of these two groups can be evaluated from measurements of the variation with latitude of the total intensity at high altitudes. Consider first the corpuscular component in both groups. It is characterized at great distances from the solar system by its isotropy and by the form of its energy spectrum, which probably follows the law E^{-2} discussed earlier (p. 89). The action of the sun's magnetic field deflects those particles with an energy lower than approximately 10^9 ev. before they can reach the earth's orbit, but it permits the more energetic particles to pass on. Of the latter, those with an energy less than 6×10^{10} ev. are subject to the influence of the earth's field, and their paths follow the curves calculated by Störmer and by Lemaître and Vallarta. We see, then, that although the radiation is isotropic out in space, it takes on a rather definite structure even before its arrival in the earth's atmosphere.

In addition to this corpuscular component, does the first group, which is insensitive to the earth's magnetic field, contain a substantial number of photons? Various experiments seem to have established that photons, if they are present at all in the primary radiation, are not numerous, as compared with charged particles. In any event, there is no equilibrium between the two types of rays, for as soon as the incident radiation reaches the upper atmosphere, profound transformations take place. This fact will assume great importance when we return to the subject of origin. As for the question of primary protons, two contrary hypotheses are possible. It may be supposed that, if protons are present at all, their role is negligible as a first approximation. On the other hand, it may be assumed that protons are present in large numbers and that they play an essential role in the subsequent formation of mesotrons.

Let us examine these two hypotheses more closely to see how each of them explains the various cosmic-ray phenomena which we have studied. According to the first hypothesis, all the cosmic-ray effects which we observe are determined by a stream of primary electrons incident upon the upper atmosphere. While focusing our attention on one of these electrons, let us follow the various transformations of its energy. From the moment of its arrival in the stratosphere, rarefied though the latter may be, the electron is subject to sudden retardation (*Bremsung*) by atoms, with attendant radiation and pair creation. This multiplication produces a shower, which attains its full development after crossing a thickness of atmosphere equivalent to around 3 feet of water. By that time the number of initial particles has been increased by a very large factor. The maximum intensity occurs at an atmospheric depth corresponding to about 3 feet of water; below this level, absorption begins to get the upper hand.

If we analyze the radiation after this first stage, we find that the initial spectrum is progressively shifted toward lower energies by the production of secondary electrons arising from pair creation by the photons. Consequently, the distinct lower limit of 10^9 ev., which characterized the initial spectrum, is soon washed out, and a very soft group of electrons appears. The rest of the energy spectrum is not subject to great changes.

Among the secondary particles produced in the showers, there is, besides electrons, a large number of photons. The constant transformations of these two types of particles into one another leads to an equilibrium between them. Various calculations have been made in order to evaluate the relative numbers of photons and electrons in the total radiation; all that can be said with confidence is that the energy contained in the two types of rays is of the same order of magnitude. Moreover, since they are continually being transformed into one another, the distinction between them has only an instantaneous meaning.

In addition to electrons and photons, a certain number of mesotrons may be produced in these regions, where the showers, still young, contain many particles of very great energy. However, the birth of mesotrons is still shrouded in mystery. Can they, like electrons, be created in pairs by photons, provided that the latter possess sufficient energy? The lower limit of this energy would be extremely high, and the probability of production of a mesotron pair would consequently be very small compared with that of the production of an electron pair.[9] Many attempts have been made to detect mesotron production in pairs, at high altitudes and at sea-level, by the methods of counters or expansion chambers. The results are still inconclusive because of the relative rarity of such phenomena in the lower atmosphere; however, several pairs of mesotrons have been photographed, and some coincidences due to simultaneous mesotrons have been observed, especially at high altitudes. The existence of the phenomenon is hardly in doubt, but we still cannot with certainty attribute to it the abundant production of mesotrons which takes place in the very high atmosphere.

Let us continue to follow the descent of this increasingly complex radiation through the atmosphere. First we shall examine the case of those showers whose initial electron has an energy less than 10^{13} ev. These showers soon diminish in intensity; i.e., their total energy at a given depth in the atmosphere decreases as we go to lower levels. The energy which they lose is completely transformed into energy of ionization. If we wish to know what ultimately becomes of

[9] Calculations of the probability of mesotron pair production lead to very different values, dependent on the assumptions made as to the nature of these particles (especially the so-called "spin," or rotational momentum, which they are supposed to possess).

this energy, we must bear in mind that the ions recombine, emitting ultra-violet or light rays; and these, in turn, being absorbed in the surrounding atmosphere, finally contribute to the thermal agitation of the air molecules. The showers are thus progressively attenuated and, at levels which are more or less deep, depending upon their energy, at last disappear altogether. It should not be forgotten, however, that in regions where their energy is still great, the showers create particles so penetrating that they easily traverse the entire atmosphere. These are the mesotrons which, if they live long enough, arrive at the ground, bringing with them a small portion of the initial electron's energy. It is probable that the energy transmitted in this way through the atmosphere does not exceed 1 or 2 per cent of the initial energy.

If, on the other hand, the shower is created by a primary electron of more than 10^{13} ev., it still contains, upon its arrival at the ground, a considerable number of particles, photons, and electrons. This would then be an "extensive shower," which contributes to the formation of the soft component at low altitudes. The mesotrons which it has created in the course of its descent are mixed in small proportion with its electrons and photons. On the other hand, those mesotrons which have the misfortune of disintegrating in the lower atmosphere give rise to electrons of equivalent energy, which in turn create small local showers. These "small showers" constitute the preponderant part of the soft component.

We next follow the radiation as it enters the absorbers below the atmosphere: earth and water. After a very short penetration there will be no more large showers at all, since the energy required to produce such a "persistent" shower is greater than that possessed by any of the primary particles.

Only the mesotrons, decreasing in number but not in average energy, can penetrate farther, carrying down to great depths a remnant of the initial energy. Finally, these in turn disappear; and, since the retardation due to the continual ionization along their path favors their disintegration, they end their career by giving birth to an electron which produces a small shower. Once this shower is absorbed, nothing more remains of the energy brought by the primary particle from interstellar space.

Now, let us examine the hypothesis that the primary corpuscles are, at least for the most part, protons. This type of particle interacts strongly with atomic nuclei, and we may assume that during its passage through the first few centimeters of water-equivalent in the atmosphere all of the proton's energy is used up in collisions. In order for such collisions to be probable in a highly rarefied gas, each nucleus must present an effective cross-section of rather large area to the passing subatomic projectile. As a result of "direct" collision with a nucleus, the proton is in some fashion pulverized into about ten mesotrons, positive and negative, in such numbers that the algebraic sum of their charges is one elementary positive charge, that of the initial proton.[10]

Many of the mesotrons thus created have high energies, since a proton cannot produce such an effect unless it possesses thousands of millions of electron-volts. As they descend deeper into the atmosphere, some of these newly born particles will decompose, producing electrons of high energy,

[10] In this connection it should be noted that measurements on the east-west asymmetry in the cosmic radiation show a predominance of positive charges among the primary particles. Likewise, a statistical study of the signs of the penetrating particles, the mesotrons, shows an excess of positive charges over negative ones.

which in turn create showers.[11] We are thus led to a sequence of events similar to that derived from the hypothesis of primary electrons, with the difference that the presence of mesotrons is accounted for.

In this general scheme we have not tried to account for the nuclear evaporations described elsewhere in this work. It seems probable that these phenomena result largely from the action of neutrons or of photons—at least in so far as the upper atmosphere is concerned. One thing is certain: the frequency of these evaporations increases with altitude in much the same way as does the intensity of the neutrons and also that of the soft component, which, it will be recalled, consists of electrons and photons. These nuclear effects result in the production of heavy particles, mainly protons and neutrons. The former produce dense ionization along their paths and are soon stopped; the latter travel long distances in the atmosphere before being absorbed by certain nuclei in which they induce radioactivity. Consequently, the cosmic radiation has a slow-neutron component the intensity of which varies with altitude in a manner similar to that of the soft component. It is to be noted, however, that no maximum has yet been found in the intensity curve of the neutrons. Finally, it may be expected that the mean energy of the neutrons, as well as their number, falls with decreasing altitude.

In concluding this brief review of what we have learned about the cosmic rays, it would be a mistake to forget that

[11] High-energy mesotrons, being very speedy, have only a small chance to decompose so soon after their birth. In order to explain the relative abundance of high-energy electrons in the upper levels of the atmosphere, it has been suggested that a new kind of mesotron, a "quick-decaying" mesotron, is formed in substantial numbers together with the long-lived ones (if a lifetime of a microsecond can be called ong!).

many unsolved problems remain. For all we know, the primary radiation may contain particles other than electrons or protons—particles whose effects may be limited to the very highest strata of the atmosphere, which our apparatus has not yet been able to reach.

QUESTION NO. 1 AGAIN

However, the major problem—and the most obscure one—is still Question No. 1: What is the primal origin of the cosmic rays? Let us survey briefly the principal hypotheses which have been advanced on this subject; and let us attempt, in the light of what we know about the properties of the cosmic rays, to evaluate them critically. We shall not discuss the theories which see within the solar system itself the possible source of the cosmic radiation, for the very small variations with time of the cosmic-ray intensity make this origin rather improbable. We begin, then, with the idea that at great distances from the solar system the cosmic radiation consists principally of electrons or protons or both, with an isotropic distribution and an energy spectrum of the character previously described.

Could such a stream of particles come from the stars? This seems unlikely, for two main reasons: (1) An electron current of great energy flowing from a region in which the concentration of matter is relatively high should be accompanied by a stream of photons. This does not appear to be the case for the primary cosmic radiation. (2) Electrons and protons of great energy are very rapidly absorbed by matter. Consequently, it is hard to understand how they could leave a stellar atmosphere without being stopped, at least if one regards their production as not altogether confined to the very top of such an atmosphere.

Let us, therefore, examine the hypothesis that the cosmic rays originate in regions of space where matter exists only in very low concentration. How can some particles accumulate such enormous energies, reaching as high as 10^{15} ev.? An idea which suggests itself at once is to postulate the existence of electrical fields that are immense in extent rather than in intensity. Fields of this sort would imply that there are differences of potential as high as many thousand millions of volts between points in space separated by great distances. One might, for example, suppose that our galaxy, which has an approximately central symmetry, is charged negatively at its periphery and charged positively at its center. All free electrons in interstellar space would then be impelled toward the center; and some of these would pass through the solar system, their energies depending upon their place of origin. Protons would behave similarly if subjected to fields of opposite sign. However, the following two objections can be raised to this type of hypothesis:

1. Should we not, under these conditions, observe a very marked anisotropy in the radiation, the electrons or protons streaming predominantly toward (or from) that region in the sky in the direction of which the center of our galaxy lies? Actually, however, the rays appear to come uniformly from all directions. This objection can be refuted, in so far as electrons and protons of average energy are concerned, since the magnetic fields of celestial bodies, particularly that of the sun, would deviate and mix up the rays sufficiently so that no indication of their initial direction would remain by the time they arrived at the earth. For particles of very high energy (from 10^{13} to 10^{15} ev.), on the other hand, the mixing effects should be insufficient; and for them the anisotropy should still be

observable. Preliminary experiments on the extensive atmospheric showers—which, it will be remembered, provide
the only certain evidence for these extremely energetic electrons—have not, however, shown notable variations with
time. These high-energy electrons, therefore, also appear to
be isotropically distributed in space.

2. We would have to imagine a mechanism which con-
stantly re-establishes the large differences of potential, since
the stream of cosmic-ray particles tends at each instant to
remove them. It is possible that a regulating mechanism may
be found in the evolution of our galaxy, which probably
undergoes a continuous expansion, and perhaps also in the
effects of radiation pressure on the ions of certain substances,
such as calcium, which are present in considerable quantities
in interstellar space. If we pursued these notions, however,
we would find ourselves plunged in scientific romanticism.
Additional information must be gathered before hypotheses
such as these can be put on a more solid foundation.

As we have seen, there appears to be no elementary process
capable of communicating all at once to an electron—or to
any other single particle—an energy as large as the energies
encountered in the cosmic radiation. We must, therefore,
seek a continuous process which might give rise to these
enormous energies. Besides the mechanism which we have
been considering, based on the acceleration of electrons or
protons by immense electric fields, there remains only one
other hypothesis, based on the action of magnetic fields, such
as those which may exist in the neighborhood of double stars.
This hypothesis, which has been formulated by H. Alfvén,
can be supported from a strictly theoretical point of view;
but it seems improbable that so exceptional a mechanism

should account for the very abundant radiation which reaches us from outer space. We must consequently admit once more that Question No. 1 is still unanswered.

We certainly know a great deal more about the cosmic rays than was known in the early period of investigation. But this knowledge is still so fragmentary that we have only negative indications as to their mode of origin. This should not, however, distress us in the least; for, if we knew all the answers, we would be deprived of the joy of exploring the unknown, and science would become as dull as a dead language. We should be happy in the thought that there will always be unsolved problems to stimulate our minds and challenge our ingenuity. If we apply to their solution all the power of our logic and imagination, science will not prove ungrateful.

INDEX

Absorbing plate in cloud chamber, 75

Absorption
  atmospheric, of radioactive rays, 12
  coefficient
    of alpha rays, 19, 20
    of cosmic rays, 19
  curve of, in lead, 68–70
  dependence of, on density of absorber, 58
  studied with coincidence circuit, 68–70
  by various substances, 20
  by water, 20, 21

Airplanes, cosmic-ray investigations in, 15

ALFVÉN, H., 119

Alpha-particle track in photographic plate, Pl. XIII (A)

Alpha particles
  from boron, 66
  in nuclear disintegrations, 62
  in stars, 63

Alpha rays, absorption of, 19–21

Altitude, dependence of ionization on, 17, 18

Aluminum, absorption of cosmic rays by, 20

ALVAREZ, L., 33

Amplification
  of ion discharges, 43
  of subatomic phenomena, 2

ANDERSON, C. D., 49–50, 58, 75, 86; Pls. V, VI, VII (B), X–XII (A), XVI

Atmosphere
  absorption of cosmic rays by, 19, 20, 21
  as shield
    against cosmic rays, 12, 13
    against radioactivity, 12

Atomic model, 65

Atomic number in shower production, 58

AUGER, P., 29, 38, 59, 60, 69, 73, 84, 92, 93, 109; Pls. I (A), III, VII–IX, XII (B), XIV, XIX

Aurora borealis, 24

Balloon flight, Pl. XIX

Balloons
  free, 17, 98–101, 106–9; Pl. XIX
  manned, 12, 16, 17, 98

BARNÓTHY, J., 21

Barometric effect, and mesotron intensity, 104

BENEDETTI, S. DE, 86

BENNETT, R., Pl. II

Beta rays, 21; see also Electrons, Soft component

BETHE, H., 74

BHABHA, H. J., 74

Biological effects of cosmic rays, 31, 48

BLACKETT, P. M. S., 46, 47, 49, 76

BLAU, M., 63

BOHR, N., 64

BOSTICK, W., 86; Pls. XVII, XX

BOTHE, W., 25, 27, 28

Bremsstrahlung, 55, 58, 76, 90

Bremsung, 56, 112

Bremsung radiation, 73

BRODE, R., Pls. IV, XVIII

Bursts, 59–61
  due to evaporations, 66
  energy of, 60
  and large showers, 60, 61

CAMERON, G. H., 19

CARLSON, J. F., 74, 105

Cascade-process illustrations, Pls. III, IV; see also Showers

Cascade theory, 104, 105

Charge, conservation of, 51

PLATE I

MEASURING COSMIC RAYS IN THE SWISS ALPS

The author (*left*) and his collaborator, P. Ehrenfest, set up their apparatus in the Jungfraujoch.

COSMIC-RAY LABORATORY AT THE TOP OF MOUNT EVANS, COLORADO

The laboratory is situated about $2\frac{1}{2}$ miles above sea-level (Korff)

PLATE II

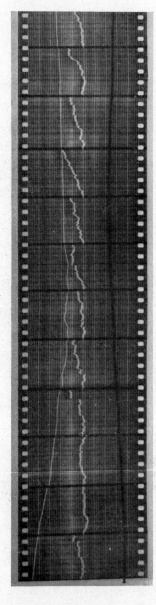

A Twelve-Hour Record of Cosmic-Ray Ionization Obtained with a Specially Designed
Ionization Chamber and Electrometer

The wavy white line records the position of the electrometer needle; the heavy black line records the barometric pressure; and the fine white line is a record of the temperature. At the end of each hour the needle returns to its zero position. The dark vertical lines mark off the hours. A sudden jump of the electrometer needle indicates a burst of ionization. (Compton, Wollan, and Bennett.)

PLATE III

A Shower Created in a Lead Plate (Not Shown)
Located above the Cloud Chamber

This shower passes through the upper compartment and strikes the platinum plate inside the chamber. Most of the electrons, possessing relatively little energy, diverge at wide angles and are readily absorbed. In the "core" of the shower, several high-energy electrons create a new shower in the metallic plate. This is an illustration of the "cascade" process. (Auger.)

PLATE IV

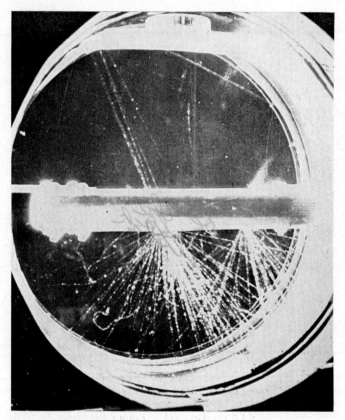

MULTIPLICATION IN A LEAD PLATE PLACED ACROSS THE
MIDDLE OF A CLOUD CHAMBER

Several electrons in the upper compartment strike the plate, and many particles emerge below. The shower at the right must have been created by a non-ionizing ray (photon), since there is no track above the plate leading to the shower's point of divergence. (Corson and Brode.)

PLATE V

STEREOSCOPIC PICTURE OF AN ELECTRON SHOWER OBSERVED ON PIKES
PEAK WITH A CLOUD CHAMBER IN A MAGNETIC FIELD

The electrons describe circular paths, the radius of curvature depending upon their energy. Positive particles and negative ones are deviated in opposite directions. In this shower there are three positrons and three negatrons, with energies ranging from 3.5×10^6 to 1.9×10^8 ev. The small circles are the tracks of low-energy electrons produced by photons which accompanied the shower electrons. In this and succeeding stereoscopic photographs, the left view is a direct image of the chamber, while the right one is a mirror image. (Anderson and Neddermeyer.)

PLATE VI

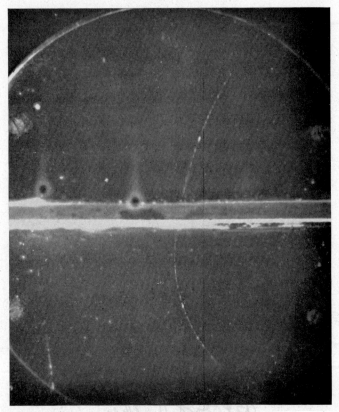

A POSITRON WITH AN ENERGY OF 6.3×10^7 EV. ENTERS A 6-MM. LEAD
PLATE FROM ABOVE AND EMERGES WITH 2.3×10^7 EV.

The cloud chamber was between the poles of a strong electromagnet. In the magnetic field, which is directed into the paper, a negative particle coming from above would be deviated toward the left; hence this is a positive particle. However, it cannot be a proton, for the track length in the lower half of the chamber is ten times as great as the possible length of a proton track with the same curvature. (Anderson.)

PLATE VII

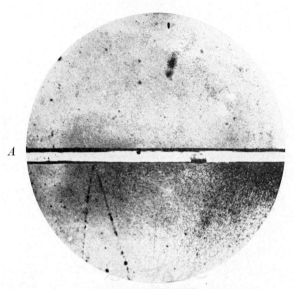

A

CREATION OF A PAIR OF ELECTRONS IN A PLATE OF PLATINUM BY A PHOTON, OF WHICH NO TRACE IS VISIBLE IN THE UPPER PART OF THE CHAMBER

(Auger and Ehrenfest)

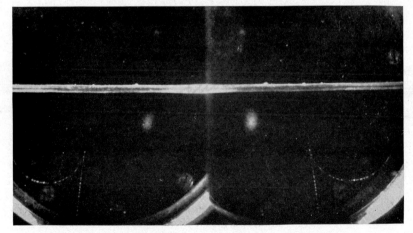

B

A POSITRON-NEGATRON PAIR PRODUCED IN THE GAS (ARGON) OF THE CHAMBER BY A COSMIC-RAY PHOTON

The negatron, possessing much less energy than the positron, has a track which is much more highly curved. (Anderson.)

PLATE VIII

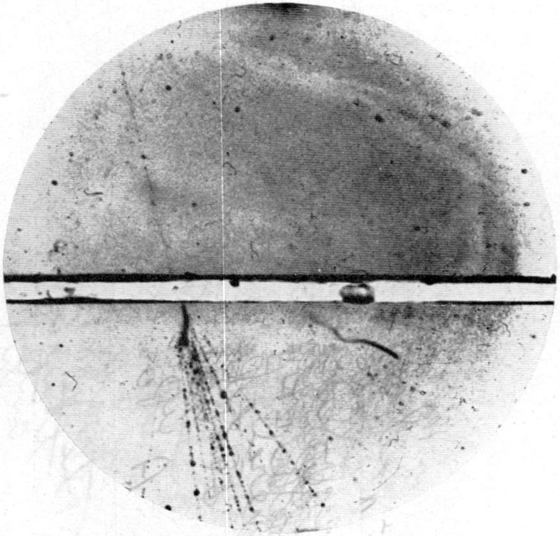

AN ELECTRON, WHOSE TRACK IS VISIBLE IN THE UPPER COMPARTMENT, CREATES A SMALL SHOWER OF EIGHT PARTICLES IN TRAVERSING THE METALLIC PLATE

(Auger and Ehrenfest)

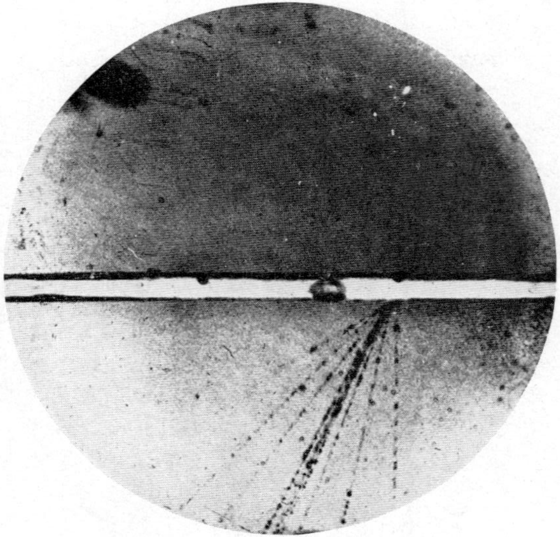

IN THIS INSTANCE A PHOTON CREATES A SHOWER OF TEN ELECTRONS IN THE PLATE: NO TRACK IS VISIBLE ABOVE THE PLATE

(Auger)

PLATE IX

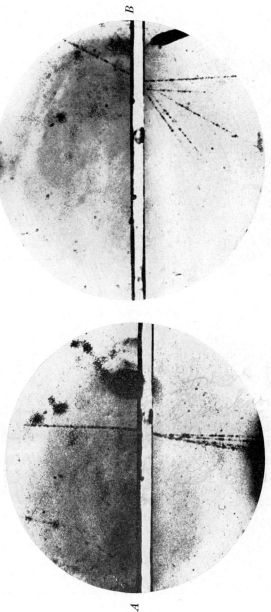

A NARROW-ANGLE SHOWER PRODUCED BY AN
IONIZING RAY

Examples of showers initiated by non-ionizing rays are
shown in Plates VII and VIII, B. (Auger.)

A SHOWER WITH TWO DISTINCT POINTS OF ORIGIN

The pair of electrons diverging from the left point may
have been created by a photon accompanying the incident
electron. (Auger.)

PLATE X

A

A Negatron Losing Much of Its Energy in a 3.5-Mm. Lead Plate

Of the tracks in the lower compartment, the least-curved one is probably due to the incident electron after its passage through the plate, while the other two are a positron-negatron pair created in the lead by the "materialization" of a photon produced in the plate. (Anderson and Neddermeyer.)

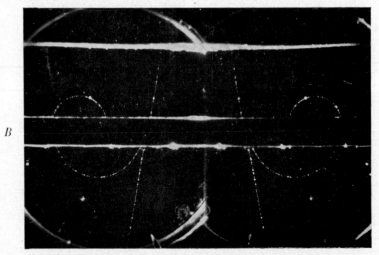

B

A Secondary Negatron (the Highly Curved Track) Produced in a
1.5-Cm. Plate of Carbon Loses 5.6×10^6 Ev. in
Traversing the Lower Plate

(Anderson and Neddermeyer)

PLATE XI

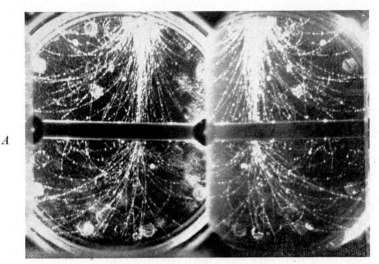

A DENSE SHOWER OF HIGH-ENERGY ELECTRONS: NORMALLY
INCIDENT ON A 1-CM. PLATE OF PLATINUM

Most of the energy is degraded into relatively low-energy electrons. (Anderson and Neddermeyer.)

A SHOWER CONTAINING A LARGE NUMBER OF ELECTRONS, WITH AN
ESTIMATED TOTAL ENERGY OF 1.5×10^{10} EV.

The number of particles probably exceeds three hundred. Showers such as this are sufficiently dense to produce the bursts of ionization observed in ionization chambers. (Anderson and Neddermeyer.)

PLATE XII

HEAVY PARTICLES PRODUCED BY DISINTEGRATION IN THE ARGON
GAS OF A CLOUD CHAMBER ON PIKES PEAK

(Anderson and Neddermeyer)

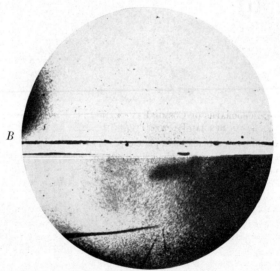

IN THE LOWER COMPARTMENT, PERHAPS IN THE GLASS WALL OF THE CHAMBER,
A NUCLEAR DISINTEGRATION IS PRODUCED BY A COSMIC-RAY PARTICLE

Several heavily ionizing particles are emitted in very divergent directions.
(Auger and Ehrenfest.)

PLATE XIII

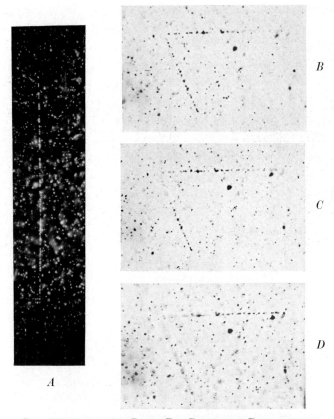

A

B

C

D

PHOTOMICROGRAPHS OF COSMIC-RAY PHENOMENA REGISTERED
IN SPECIAL PHOTOGRAPHIC EMULSIONS

  A. Track of a heavy particle from a plate exposed at an elevation of 6,700 feet.
From the spacing of the silver bromide grains and the length of the track, it is attributed to an alpha particle with a range of about 22 cm. in air. Since the stopping
power of the emulsion is 1,400 times that of air, the observed range was 0.157 mm.
Magnification 400×. (Shapiro.)

  B, C, D, three views of a twofold "star," the result of a nuclear disintegration
caused by a cosmic ray at an elevation of 12,000 feet. Both tracks appear to be due
to protons. Neither track lies flat in the emulsion. Hence, as the microscope is fo-
cused on successive layers of the emulsion, various portions of the tracks come into
view. B shows the appearance of the "star" at the surface of the emulsion; in C the
microscope was racked down to a lower plane; D was photographed at a level deep
within the emulsion. Magnification, 600×. These photomicrographs were taken
with ordinary illumination, whereas A was obtained with a dark-field condenser.
(Shapiro.)

PLATE XIV

The diagram at the left shows the arrangement with which the two pictures at the right were obtained. The expansions of the two chambers are initiated simultaneously by a coincidence between the two counters, caused by the passage of the penetrating particle.

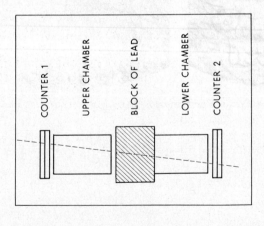

COUNTER 1

UPPER CHAMBER

BLOCK OF LEAD

LOWER CHAMBER

COUNTER 2

Two Photographs Obtained Simultaneously from Cloud Chambers Superposed One above Another and Separated by a Block of Lead Several Decimeters Thick

Above and below the block can be seen the track of the same particle, deviated but slightly. This particle is much too penetrating to be an electron. The whole system of two chambers is placed in a strong magnetic field (electromagnet of Bellevue, in Paris) which determines a visible and measurable curvature of the tracks. From the difference of curvature between the upper and the lower track, the loss of energy suffered by the particle during the traversal of the lead block can be calculated. (Auger and Ehrenfest.)

PLATE XV

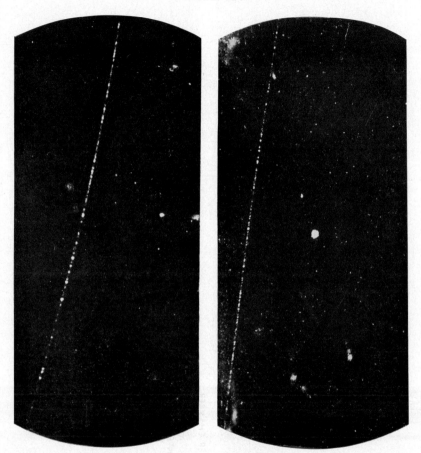

CLOUD-CHAMBER PHOTOGRAPHS OF MESOTRON TRACKS IN A MAGNETIC FIELD

The track at the left, showing appreciable curvature, is that of a positive mesotron with an energy of 5.48×10^8 ev. The track at the right, with a slight curvature in the opposite sense, was produced by a negative mesotron with 2.48×10^9 ev. (D. Hughes.)

PLATE XVI

A Mesotron Passes through a Geiger-Müller Counter Placed inside a
Cloud Chamber, and Comes To Rest in the Gas, Which
Is a Mixture of Argon and Helium

(Anderson and Neddermeyer)

PLATE XVII

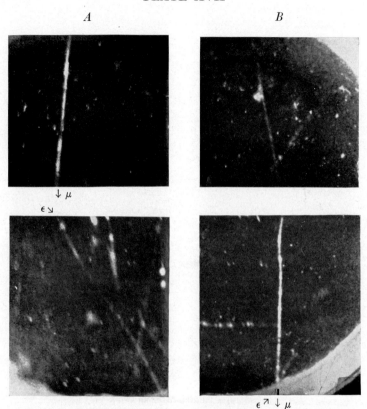

PHOTOGRAPHS TAKEN AT THE TOP OF MOUNT EVANS, WITH 12.7 CM. OF LEAD ABOVE THE CLOUD CHAMBER

A. A slow mesotron or a slow proton enters the lead plate, and a particle with the specific ionization of a fast electron emerges below at an angle of 45° with the direction of the first track. A possible interpretation is that a slow mesotron disintegrates and gives rise to the electron below. (Bostick.)

B. A mesotron markedly increasing its ionization in passing through 1.3 cm. of lead. It is possible that the faint track in the bottom of the chamber is the decay electron of the slow mesotron. (Bostick.)

PLATE XVIII

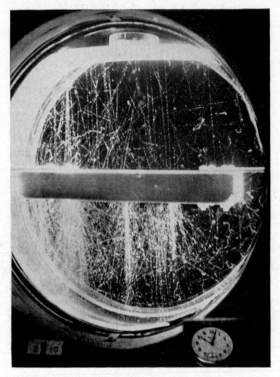

EXTENSIVE ATMOSPHERIC (OR AUGER-) SHOWER CONTAIN-
ING MANY HIGH-ENERGY ELECTRONS

Note the parallelism of the vertical tracks, which indicates that the shower must
have originated high above the apparatus. (Corson and Brode.)

PLATE XIX

A

B

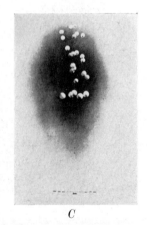

C

BALLOON FLIGHT OF JANUARY, 1943, CONDUCTED BY THE AUTHOR, SCHEIN,
AND ROGOZINSKI FOR THE MEASUREMENT OF EXTENSIVE (OR
AUGER-) SHOWERS IN THE STRATOSPHERE

A. The balloons are assembled on Stagg Field at the University of Chicago, Chicago, Illinois. In the foreground can be seen the long frame which was required for the wide separation of the cosmic-ray counters.

B. The large cluster of balloons as it is about to be released.

C. The balloon train sails into the sky after its release. Suspended below the balloons is the frame supporting the counters and recording apparatus.

PLATE XX

In This Cloud-Chamber Picture, Taken at an Altitude of About $2\frac{1}{2}$ Miles, a Group of Particles Coming from the Top (*left*) Strikes a 1.3-Cm. Lead Plate, and Two of Them Penetrate without Producing Any Secondaries

Moreover, the particles show a specific ionization high enough to be slow mesotrons or slow protons. It is probable, therefore, that these particles are not electrons but are a shower of mesotrons or protons. (Bostick.)

PLATE XXI

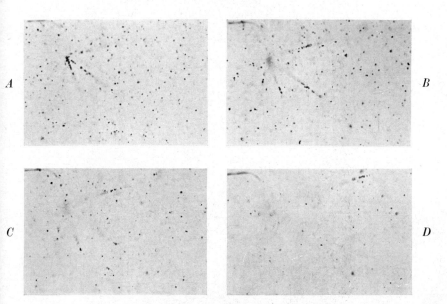

A Cosmic-Ray "Star" Resulting from a Nuclear Evaporation in Which
Four Heavy Charged Particles Were Emitted
from the Excited Nucleus

The star appears in three dimensions, and not all parts of it can be seen at once through the high-power lens of the microscope. Photomicrograph A shows the origin of the tracks, whereas B, C, and D are views observed in successively deeper layers of emulsion, showing the tracks as they radiate outward from the center. In D, only the end of the uppermost, and longest, track can be seen. Magnification, 600×. (Shapiro.)

PLATE XXII

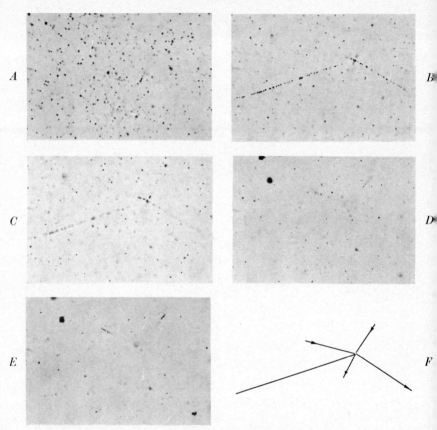

A FIVEFOLD "STAR" OBSERVED IN A PHOTOGRAPHIC PLATE WHICH WAS
EXPOSED AT AN ALTITUDE OF 12,000 FEET ABOVE SEA-LEVEL

The tracks radiate from a point which lies within the emulsion (see *B* and *C*). *A* is a view of a surface layer, showing a track sloping steeply upward. Measurement of its grain-spacing indicates that this track is due to an alpha particle. In *B* two long tracks come into focus, whereas in *C*, *D*, and *E* a pair of steep, downward-sloping tracks become visible. The four latter tracks are probably those of protons. (Magnification, 600×.) It is likely that, in addition to these charged particles, five or more neutrons were also emitted in this nuclear disintegration. (The latter are non-ionizing particles and therefore leave no tracks.) Since a total of about ten particles were "evaporated," this event is attributed to a cosmic ray of great energy, probably between 50,000,000 and 100,000,000 ev. Line-drawing *F* indicates the orientation of the tracks as they would appear in projection. The arrows point toward the surface of the emulsion. (Shapiro.)